THE COMMONWEALTH AND INTERNATIONAL LIBRARY
Joint Chairmen of the Honorary Editorial Advisory Board

SIR ROBERT ROBINSON, O.M., F.R.S., LONDON

DEAN ATHELSTAN SPILHAUS, MINNESOTA

Publisher: ROBERT MAXWELL, M.C., M.P.

MATHEMATICS DIVISION

General Editors: W. J. LANGFORD, E. A. MAXWELL

STATISTICS FOR THE TEACHER

STATISTICS
for the Teacher

DOUGLAS M. McINTOSH
C.B.E., LL.D., M.A., B.Sc., B.Ed., Ph.D., F.R.S.E., F.E.I.S.

Principal, Moray House College of Education
Edinburgh, Scotland

PERGAMON PRESS

OXFORD · LONDON · EDINBURGH · NEW YORK
TORONTO · SYDNEY · PARIS · BRAUNSCHWEIG

Pergamon Press Ltd., Headington Hill Hall, Oxford
4 & 5 Fitzroy Square, London W.1

Pergamon Press (Scotland) Ltd., 2 & 3 Teviot Place, Edinburgh 1

Pergamon Press Inc., 44–01 21st Street, Long Island City, New York 11101

Pergamon of Canada Ltd., 6 Adelaide Street East, Toronto, Ontario

Pergamon Press (Aust.) Pty. Ltd., 20–22 Margaret Street,
Sydney, New South Wales

Pergamon Press S.A.R.L., 24 rue des Écoles, Paris 5e

Vieweg & Sohn GmbH, Burgplatz 1, Braunschweig

Printed in Great Britain by Blackie & Son Ltd., Glasgow

Contents

Introduction

EXAMINATIONS and tests are an essential part of modern education. It is vital, therefore, not only that these are carefully constructed and marked, but also that the marks themselves are properly interpreted and used. This book aims to help practising and prospective teachers to a fuller understanding of the significance and legitimate use of examination marks.

The application of elementary statistics to examination marks involves only arithmetic, Mathematical knowledge is not essential. Even the calculation of a square root can be avoided by the use of tables.

Based on lectures delivered over many years to teachers both in this country and in Canada, the material here presented has been found adequate to give many a better insight into examining. For those who wish to pursue the study of statistics further, other books are available. The treatment here is essentially simple: at the start the different methods of calculation have been explained, but in the later chapters formulae have been introduced without explanation.

Exercises have been included throughout the book. One or two follow each topic to ensure that the text has been understood. Selected from actual results of school and external examinations they illustrate exactly the type of problem a teacher may have to handle.

CHAPTER I

Measurement in Education

Counting and Measuring

Counting and measuring are not the same. Primitive man found it essential to count; he had to know, for example, the number of sheep in his flock and also the size of his family. Measurement, on the other hand, was less essential and less exact; the height of an animal was denoted as so many hands, and the reference to feet in measuring distance is obvious.

The essential difference is that while counting is exact, measuring is approximate. There is only one answer to the number of pupils in a class or of candidates for an examination, whereas the length of a line as measured by an ordinary ruler is not nearly as accurate as when measured by an instrument which is exact to a thousandth of an inch. Similarly the weight of an object can be found approximately by a spring balance or more exactly by an extremely sensitive instrument.

Examination marks are measurements and therefore although usually denoted by whole numbers are, nevertheless, approximations. They do not even have the accuracy of physical measurement such as length measured by a ruler. The approximate nature of examination marks should always be remembered.

There are occasions when enumeration or counting appear to be used. Some tests, such as arithmetic attainment tests, allocate one mark to each correct sum and the total score represents the number of sums correctly worked. There is an underlying assumption that each sum is of equal difficulty, or that all errors are of the same magnitude; neither of which is commonly true. Therefore, while enumeration is a convenient method of arriving at a score, the result is still only an approximation.

Direct and Indirect Measurement

A distinction must also be made between direct and indirect measurement. Length and weight can be measured directly. A line is measured by a ruler and the weight of an object is found by placing it on a balance. Temperature, on the other hand, is measured indirectly, normally by the height of a column of mercury in a thermometer.

Measurements in education are always indirect. An arithmetic mark normally represents the pupil's performance on a sample number of questions. In an arithmetic examination the teacher seldom checks which addition, subtraction, multiplication and division combinations have been included: it may quite well be that some of the most difficult are omitted.

The choice of sample in some subjects is much more difficult than in others. In English literature, for example, a pupil's ability to answer a particular set of questions provides little guarantee that he knows even a limited field thoroughly—"to examine literature is as impossible as to imprison sunbeams".

Examination marks are sometimes used for purposes beyond the examiner's intention. This applies particularly to the assumption that a high mark in one examination will guarantee success in others: there is little evidence that Leaving Certificate marks are good forecasts of marks in University examinations.

Units

Measurements can be made in different units and it is always necessary to state clearly the unit of measurement used. For example, it is not sufficient to say that the length of a line is 6. The unit, inches or feet as the case may be, must be clearly stated.

It is possible to measure the length of an object and to express its length in different units: a line 12 inches long may be referred to as being one foot in length. Similarly, temperature can be expressed in degrees centigrade or degrees fahrenheit. Measurements may be expressed as fractions or percentages.

Measurements can be combined or compared only if they are expressed in the same units. It is not possible to tell whether a temperature of 60 degrees centigrade is higher than one of 85 degrees fahrenheit unless they are brought to the same units.

In educational measurements, also, the units must always be the same if marks are to be compared or added. With percentage marks there is an assumption that each individual unit is the same. This is not generally the case. It is normally much easier to increase a score within the limits of 1–10% than within the limits of 90–100%.

Different examiners normally have different standards of marking. It has been shown over and over again that two examiners seldom mark on the same standard or with the same units: indeed there is ample proof that the same examiner at different times may use different units of measurement.

Awarding percentage, or individual, marks is not the only means of measurement in education. Categoric marks can be usefully employed. The scale A, B, C, D, E is sometimes used, A indicating an exceptionally good and E a very poor performance.

A pupil's mark may also be denoted by a place in a band of marks. For the Scottish Certificate of Education examinations teachers were asked to estimate not the actual mark but whether a pupil fell into one of several bands; for example, 60–70%.

Quotients are also used to denote a pupil's position on a scale. The best known are intelligence quotients (I.Q.s) and these take into account not only the pupil's performance on a test but also his age at the time of taking the test.

Zero

Normally measurements are made from the same point or zero which is sometimes known as the origin. Eight inches long means that there are eight separate inches between 0 and 8, but zero need not necessarily be the origin. For example, a golfer sometimes reckons his score in strokes above and below what he anticipates his average score per hole will be. If his average is four strokes per hole and he takes five for the first hole, his score will be counted as one. If, at the second hole he scores four his total is still one. If, however, he takes three at the second hole he reckons his score for that hole as minus one, and his total for the two holes zero, which means four for each hole.

This example shows that negative numbers can be used in measurement. The most common example is in the measurement of temperature where $-10°C$ means $10°$ below freezing point.

The normal practice in awarding examination marks is to use a numerical scale from 0 upwards. Marks are often converted into a percentage of the total. This can be quite misleading because the examiner may not use the complete range of measurement. For example, the marks may be out of 100 but it is often noticeable that the range 90–100 is seldom used in secondary school examination marks. Percentage marks, therefore, can give a wrong impression of what the marks mean.

With quotients, the zero of the scale is often taken to be the average. For example, with I.Q.s the origin is regarded as 100; I.Q. 80 is not generally thought of as being 80 marks above zero, but tends to be thought of as 20 below the average.

If the origin is taken at a high enough point it may quite well be that negative marks could arise. The interpretation of a negative mark, while clear to the mathematician, would be almost meaningless to the layman, and therefore there is little support for the use of negative marks in connection with examinations.

CHAPTER II

Interpretation of Marks

A MARK by itself has no meaning. There is a tradition, from which many teachers and parents find it difficult to depart, of taking 50 or 50% to be the pass mark. Fifty per cent might be a good mark or a bad mark depending on a variety of factors such as the difficulty of the examination, the ability of the class, and the standard of marking of the examiner.

Another somewhat meaningless method of denoting the worth of a test performance is to express the mark as being "out of" the maximum mark. For example, 80 out of 150 means little: more needs to be known before it can be judged a good, average or poor mark.

It is not possible to interpret a mark unless something is known about the marks of other pupils who sat the examination. For example, 50% may be good in one case and poor in another. Take the following:

$$\text{Set A} \quad 20 \quad 30 \quad 40 \quad \underline{50} \quad 60$$
$$\text{Set B} \quad \underline{50} \quad 60 \quad 70 \quad 80 \quad 90$$

In Set A, 50 appears to be a good mark whereas in set B it is the lowest. Reference must be made to the average mark in each case. In set A 50 is above the average whereas in set B it is below the average.

Even in two sets of marks with the same average, identical marks may have a different meaning. For example:

Set E	10	20	30	40	50̲̲	60	70̲	80	90
Set F	30	35	40	45	50̲̲	55	60	65	70̲

In both sets the average mark is 50, but the mark of 70 has a different interpretation in each: it is the third best mark in set E whereas in set F it is the highest mark.

Further, one must know something about the spread or scatter of the marks in order to assess the value of a mark. In set E marks are much more widely spread than in set F.

The following sets of marks illustrate both how their average, or mean as it is called in statistical phraseology, and their scatter are necessary to determine the value of a particular mark.

In each group there are 36 pupils, each "x" denoting a pupil.

Set G   FIGURE 1

```
                              x
                    x    x    x
               x    x    x    x    x
          x    x    x    x    x    x    x
     x    x    x    x    x    x    x    x    x
x    x    x    x    x    x    x    x    x    x    x
─────────────────────────────────────────────────
45   50   55   60   65   70   75   80   85   90   95
```

Set H   FIGURE 2

```
                    x
                    x
               x    x    x
          x    x    x    x    x
          x    x    x    x    x
     x    x    x    x    x    x    x
     x    x    x    x    x    x    x
     x    x    x    x    x    x    x
     ─────────────────────────────
     35   40   45   50   55   60   65
```

The respective averages of the two groups are 70 and 50 and the marks are much more widespread in set G than in set H. Suppose these are the marks of the same class in two examinations, G being arithmetic and H English. Suppose further that a boy John is first in arithmetic, but has the average mark in English and Mary has the average mark in arithmetic, but is first in English. John's total mark is 95+50, that is 145, whereas Mary's total mark is 70+65 that is 135. Clearly John's first in arithmetic seems to be more valuable than Mary's first in English.

Some may object that the standard of marking in arithmetic is higher than the standard of marking in English. This might be remedied by deducting 20 marks from each arithmetic mark; the respective totals would then be:

$$\text{John} \quad 75+50=125$$

$$\text{Mary} \quad 50+65=115$$

Even when the standard of the marking of two examinations is apparently made equivalent the spread or scatter of marks in arithmetic tells when the marks are added.

The value of a mark cannot therefore be determined unless both the average and the scatter of the marks is known. Marks should not be compared or combined unless the standard of marking and the spread or scatter of marks are the same.

Perhaps the educationist rather than the statistician, however, might query any combining of marks. What significance has the total of an English mark and an arithmetic mark? Even worse is the old practice of combining all the pupil's class marks to give his average mark. If the average and scatters of the marks in all subjects are made the same, the total of the marks may have some statistical significance. It is doubtful whether it has any educational significance.

CHAPTER III

Arranging Marks

IN THE previous chapter it was shown that a pupil's mark has meaning only when its position relative to others is known. Where the number of entries is 20 or less the most useful arrangement is a list in descending order of magnitude. The following are the marks of twenty pupils in a class examination:

TABLE 1. MARKS OF 20 PUPILS

Pupil	Mark	Pupil	Mark	Pupil	Mark	Pupil	Mark
A	62	F	30	K	60	P	25
B	50	G	60	L	75	Q	40
C	36	H	48	M	50	R	90
D	45	I	60	N	85	S	36
E	54	J	78	O	32	T	80

It is not easy to see from this table of marks what a score of 50 signifies.

The arrangement of marks in descending order of magnitude shows the position of each mark relative to the others:

90	50
85	50
80	48
78	45
75	40
62	36
60	36
60	32
60	30
54	25

A mark of 50 is now seen to be somewhere near the middle of the group of marks.

Checking Marks

Most teachers probably find it easier to deal with marks when arranged in columns rather than rows. Although a column of marks is generally added from the bottom upwards, research has shown that slightly greater accuracy is obtained by adding downwards. Every figure, however, should be checked. When a set of marks is copied they should always be checked. Similarly, every calculation should be repeated using, wherever possible, a different method. For example, additions should be checked by adding upwards and downwards.

Frequency Distribution

Where the number of entries is larger than about 20, a list of individual marks is cumbersome, particularly where there is a number of identical entries.

The following 40 marks were scored by a class in an arithmetic test:

8, 6, 5, 2, 10, 9, 3, 2, 1, 6, 7, 5, 4, 5, 0, 2, 5, 6, 7, 4,

3, 4, 6, 8, 5, 7, 4, 3, 5, 3, 4, 9, 5, 7, 6, 5, 3, 1, 4, 6.

It is difficult to see from the list how the marks are distributed. It would be much more useful to see at a glance how many pupils scored 10, how many scored 9 and so on.

One method is to arrange the marks in descending order and to record by tallies (/) opposite the respective marks the number of pupils who scored these marks. When five tallies are to be recorded, four are marked thus //// and the fifth is made across the four thus ⦀⧸. The tallies are then totalled as follows:

Mark	Tallies	Frequencies
10	/	1
9	//	2
8	//	2
7	////	4
6	///// /	6
5	///// ///	8
4	///// /	6
3	· /////	5
2	///	3
1	//	2
0	/	1
		――
		40

The number of pupils at each mark is known as the *frequency*, generally denoted by *f*, and the arrangement is known as the *frequency distribution*. The *range* of a distribution is the difference between the highest and lowest marks. In the above distribution the range is 10–0, i.e. 10; in the distribution in Table 1 the range is 90–25, i.e. 65.

Note that all figures must be checked. The simplest method of checking the tally is to repeat the operation placing a dot at the foot of each tally.

Exercise

Prepare frequency distributions for the following marks:

1.	7	7	6	7	1
	10	11	7	11	3
	10	11	10	10	4
	6	6	11	9	
	6	8	9	5	
	10	8	11	3	
	9	11	12	5	
	8	7	12	4	

2.

43	45	41	8	59
55	47	37	15	57
24	59	46	57	68
45	42	40	53	66
51	33	53	52	61
44	46	25	48	63
48	40	45	48	53
36	25	14	67	62

Class-interval

When the range of marks is greater than about 15, a frequency distribution of individual marks becomes unwieldy.

Table 2 gives the I.Q.s for 40 pupils.

TABLE 2

Pupil	I.Q.	Pupil	I.Q.	Pupil	I.Q.	Pupil	I.Q.
A	112	K	101	U	106	EE	111
B	88	L	87	V	98	FF	83
C	115	M	98	W	109	GG	123
D	131	N	103	X	94	HH	108
E	105	O	90	Y	108	II	92
F	91	P	115	Z	89	JJ	132
G	85	Q	113	AA	105	KK	90
H	106	R	93	BB	118	LL	110
I	93	S	83	CC	103	MM	100
J	102	T	103	DD	89	NN	113

The I.Q.s range from the lowest 83 to the highest 132, a range of 49. The distribution of marks can be conveniently arranged by dividing the range into ten or more intervals and showing the number of marks in each interval. If the interval is taken as 5 points of I.Q. starting from 130–134 and finishing with 80–84, there will be 11 such class-intervals, as they are called. The interval 80–84 includes the five marks, 80, 81, 82, 83 and 84 and the next interval is 85–89.

As a general rule there should be not more than 20 and a minimum of 10 class-intervals in a distribution.

The method of finding the frequency distribution is the same as that in the example for individual marks.

Class-interval	Tally	Frequency
130–134	//	2
125–129		0
120–124	/	1
115–119	///	3
110–114	̶H̶H̶	5
105–109	̶H̶H̶ //	7
100–104	̶H̶H̶ /	6
95–99	//	2
90–94	̶H̶H̶ //	7
85–89	̶H̶H̶	5
80–84	//	2
	TOTAL	40

For percentages, the range of the class-intervals is often conveniently taken as 10, starting 0–9. *Note:* the limits of the interval are *inclusive*.

Terman, the American psychologist, suggested the following classification of I.Q.s:

Above 140 near genius or genius

120–140 very superior intelligence

110–120 superior intelligence

90–110 normal or average intelligence

80–90 dullness, rarely classifiable as feeble mindedness

70–80 borderline deficiency, sometimes classifiable as dullness, often as feeble mindedness

Below 70 definite feeble mindedness

It should be noted that here the class-intervals are not of uniform size. This arrangement is sometimes adopted when the frequencies at the extreme ends of the distribution are small.

In Terman's classification the interval 80–90 includes I.Q.s from 80 up to, but not including, 90. This method of stating class-intervals is confusing and should be avoided.

Exercises

Prepare a frequency distribution for the following marks taking 5 as the class-interval in question 1, and 7 as the class-interval in question 2.

1.
46	36	64	34	24	16	75	54	64
48	46	23	23	54	8	96	78	79
30	40	11	43	50	20	89	88	
47	33	23	31	53	49	84	55	
54	30	55	42	54	53	99	76	

2.
68	64	74	64	53	46	75	81	76
77	70	68	56	68	36	73	93	84
60	59	60	66	77	47	74	91	
66	68	62	65	52	86	86	83	
72	73	64	67	75	78	90	85	

The Diagrammatic Representation of Data

The aim of the statistical organization of educational data is to give a clear indication of the pattern of the marks as a whole. In the main, statistics are concerned with groups of marks and give little information about individual marks apart from the group in which they fall.

One of the simplest and most effective methods of representing the frequency distribution in graphical form is the *histogram*. The histogram for the frequency distribution of the I.Q.s in Table 2 is shown in Figure 3.

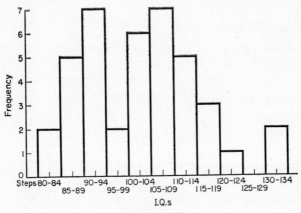

FIGURE 3

Steps in the Construction of a Histogram

1. Draw a horizontal line, along which mark off units to represent the class-intervals. For example, each unit is 5 points of I.Q. It is usual to start with the class-intervals of lowest value.

   Denote what the unit on the axis represents, e.g. I.Q.s.

2. Draw a vertical line through the extreme end of the horizontal axis along which mark off units to represent the frequencies of the entries in each of the class-intervals.

   Denote what the units on the axis represent, e.g. 0, 1, 2, etc.

3. Draw rectangles with class-intervals units as base and the respective frequencies as height.

Exercise

Construct a histogram from the following marks using a class-interval of 5:

66	65	79	63	53	40	82	79	79
72	74	59	53	76	34	90	87	89
57	65	49	63	76	42	88	94	
67	59	53	69	59	77	90	80	
72	66	66	70	78	78	95	86	

The histogram for the frequency distribution of individual marks is drawn in a similar way except that the marks are at the mid-point of the base of the rectangles. For example, the histogram for the frequency distribution on page 10 is shown in Figure 4.

Frequency Polygon

Another method of representing a frequency distribution graphically is what is known as the *frequency polygon*. The first two steps are identical with those used in the construction of the histogram. The third step is as follows:

Step 3

Directly above the point on the axis representing the mid-point of each class-interval, or each individual mark, plot a point at a height proportional to the frequencies. These points are joined.

The frequency polygon for the distribution on page 10 is shown in Figure 5.

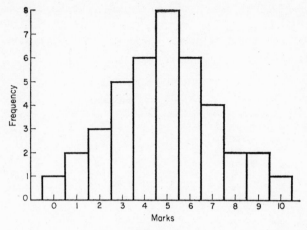

FIGURE 4

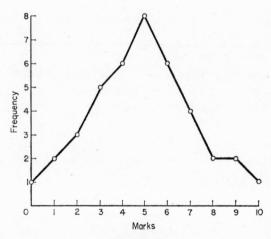

FIGURE 5

16   STATISTICS FOR THE TEACHER

One advantage of the frequency polygon lies in the fact that it
can give a clearer picture of two contrasted frequency distributions. For example, the frequency polygons for the distribution
of the English and arithmetic marks in Table 3 are shown in
Figure 6.

TABLE 3

Class-interval	Frequency Arithmetic	English
95–99	2	0
90–94	3	1
85–89	3	2
80–84	5	3
75–79	6	5
70–74	7	8
65–69	7	11
60–64	7	12
55–59	7	10
50–54	6	9
45–49	6	5
40–44	5	3
35–39	4	1
30–34	2	0
TOTALS	70	70

The frequency polygon for the English marks is less spread out
than that for arithmetic. This variation of pattern is character-
istic of English and arithmetic marks.

Frequency Curve

Where the points of the frequency polygon lie along a curve
this can be drawn freehand. See Figure 7.

Skewness

In a graphical representation of a frequency distribution the
lack of symmetry may be of significance and may be due to
special factors.

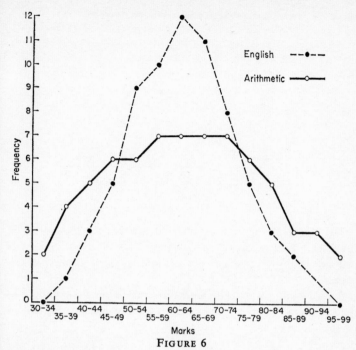

FIGURE 6

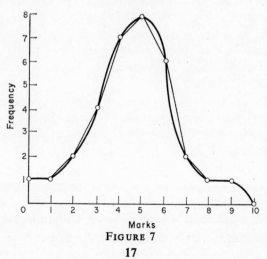

FIGURE 7

17

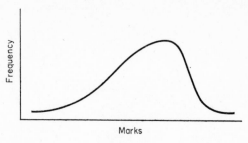

FIGURE 8

The marks in Figure 8 are massed towards the higher end of the scale. This is known as skewness. The distribution in this instance is skewed towards the left and is called negative skewness.

A distribution where the marks are massed at the high end of the scale and spread out gradually at the low end may be caused by several factors.

(a) The examination may have been too easy for the class, the majority of the pupils securing high marks.

(b) The examination may have no headroom, that is the abler pupils have too little opportunity to score beyond a certain score. The concluding questions may be too difficult for the best pupils.

(c) The examination may be of the qualifying type such as a leaving certificate examination where the intention is to find those who have been able to reach the pass level of attainment.

The curve in Figure 9 is skewed positively, or to the right, when the marks are massed at the low end of the scale and spread out gradually at the high end.

Factors which cause a distribution of this type include:

(a) An examination with no simple questions.

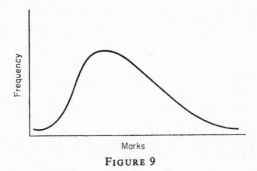

FIGURE 9

(b) The examination may be too difficult for the children to whom it is set.

(c) The examination may have been constructed to differentiate the able pupils, e.g. a competitive examination.

Construction of Examinations

Examinations should be constructed with a definite purpose in mind. In some instances the distribution of marks may reveal the success with which this purpose has been achieved.

An examination or test can be constructed to give any desired distribution.

Interpretation of Distributions

Three factors may be taken into account in interpreting the distribution of marks:

(a) The nature of the examination.
   Figures 8 and 9 showed skewed distributions which could be due to the ease or difficulty of the questions.

(b) The type of group sitting the examinations.
   A class of very able pupils will give a completely different distribution from a class of dull and backward pupils sitting the same examination.

(c) The Marking Scheme.

Teachers differ in their attitude to errors. Some may deduct many marks for errors in addition in the arithmetic examination and some may be lenient with such mistakes; the distribution of marks by two such teachers will clearly be different.

Exercises

1. Arrange the following marks in rank order. How many pupils have scored marks (a) below 7, (b) above 8, and (c) between 5 and 8?

5	7	9	8	7	7
7	5	9	8	6	9
6	0	8	9	9	5
2	5	6	7	7	
6	9	10	5	7	

2. Prepare a frequency distribution for the following class marks. Which mark has the highest frequency?

5	5	8	9	7	8
3	5	8	4	10	5
4	2	4	8	8	8
3	5	8	2	2	
1	8	8	2	4	

3. Prepare a frequency distribution for the following set of English marks for a class of 40 pupils. Take a class-interval of size 7, with 42–48 as the lowest interval and 91–97 as the highest interval. What are the frequencies corresponding to the intervals (a) 56–62, and (b) 77–83?

73	50	77	81	58	62	68	84
55	44	47	94	69	68	47	51
78	62	55	53	79	81	86	78
88	55	69	53	58	87	82	55
68	71	50	76	74	53	56	78

4. Prepare a frequency distribution of the following arithmetic marks. Take a class-interval of size 9. How many pupils have marks between 62 and 72?

77	50	65	79	70	36	69	97
44	55	59	85	80	74	42	61
73	57	64	50	62	79	75	91
68	50	64	44	64	76	91	69
59	68	50	68	66	55	50	70

5. Construct frequency polygons from the marks in questions 1 and 2, pages 10 and 11

6. Construct histograms from the marks in questions 1 and 2, page 13.

CHAPTER IV

The Average, or Mean

A SINGLE measure to represent a group of scores is often required. For example, two teachers marking the same set of examination scripts, even with a marking scheme, are liable to have different standards of marking, and it is necessary to have some means of indicating the standard to which each marks. Again, it is sometimes necessary to compare the performance in an examination of one class with another. The most convenient measure of the standard of marking or of the standard of attainment is the average or arithmetic mean. The golfer who goes round in 72 describes his score as level fours which is another method of describing the average or the mean score for each of the 18 holes.

The average or mean can be calculated for each of the three types of distribution illustrated in the previous chapter, namely a list of marks, a frequency distribution of individual marks, and a frequency distribution of grouped data.

Mean of List of Marks

The mean of a list of marks is found by adding up the marks and dividing by the number of marks. For the following list of marks:

$$73, 70, 68, 63, 60, 56, 53, 50, 48, 43, 40, 36$$

the mean is $\frac{660}{12} = 55$.

This may be represented symbolically by $M = \frac{\Sigma X}{N}$ where X

represents a mark, ΣX is the sum of the marks,* and N is the number of marks.

Exercises

1. The following marks were scored by twenty children in a mental arithmetic test. Calculate the average mark.

7	6	9	6
4	5	3	7
12	10	11	7
3	8	2	9
7	6	10	8

2. A class scored the following marks in an English test. Find the mean mark for the class.
   35, 49, 25, 12, 48, 14, 40, 28, 18, 44, 50, 29, 46, 9, 30, 10, 23, 8, 33.

3. Find the mean of the marks in Table 1, page 8.

Mean from Frequency Distribution of Individual Marks

TABLE 4

Mark (X)	Frequency (f)
10	1
9	2
8	3
7	4
6	5
5	8
4	7
3	3
2	3
1	3
0	1
TOTAL	40

To find the mean, the sum of all the marks has to be calculated. This is found by first multiplying the marks by their frequencies,

* The capital letter sigma of the Greek alphabet denotes a summation, i.e. ΣX is the sum of the X's.

i.e. $f \times X$. There are 2 marks of 9, contributing 18 marks. The respective products are 10, 18, 24, 28, 30, 40, 28, 9, 6, 3 and 0.

The sum of the marks is 196; hence the mean is $\dfrac{196}{40}$ which is 4·9.

Expressed in symbols the calculation is $M = \dfrac{\Sigma f X}{N}$. The layout of the calculation is:

X	f	fX	
5	1	5	
4	3	12	$M = \dfrac{\Sigma f X}{N}$
3	8	24	
2	2	4	
1	1	1	$= \dfrac{46}{16}$
0	1	0	
TOTALS	16	46	$= 2\cdot88$

Exercises

1. A class was given 10 mental arithmetic sums as a test resulting in the following marks.

   10, 4, 7, 3, 7, 5, 9, 2, 10, 6, 6, 4, 4, 8, 3, 8, 8, 8, 5, 2, 2, 4, 5, 6, 9, 7, 7, 5, 10.

   Find the mean mark for the class.

2. Thirty-seven pupils scored the following marks in a test of 20 mechanical arithmetic sums:

   19, 18, 14, 10, 7, 13, 13, 16, 16, 15, 9, 9, 12, 17, 20, 6, 13, 8, 15, 18, 20, 12, 9, 5, 16, 14, 13, 5, 9, 16, 17, 14, 7, 8, 10, 13, 12.

   Find the frequency of each mark and the mean mark for the class.

Change of Origin

Where the frequencies and marks are large the calculation can be simplified by changing the origin of measurement.

The marks in Table 4 are measured from 0. Suppose, however, these marks were measured from 5. They would become, 5, 4, 3, 2, 1, 0, -1, -2, -3, -4, -5. The calculation would become:

Mark		Frequency	
X (Origin 0)	x (Origin 5)	f	fx
10	5	1	5
9	4	2	8
8	3	3	9
7	2	4	8
6	1	5	5
5	0	8	0
4	−1	7	−7
3	−2	3	−6
2	−3	3	−9
1	−4	3	−12
0	−5	1	−5
TOTALS		40	+35
			−39

$$\Sigma fx = 35 - 39$$
$$= -4$$

Hence the mean is $\dfrac{-4}{40} = -0 \cdot 1$. But this is measured from 5 as origin. The mean measured from zero is $5 + (-0 \cdot 1) = 5 - 0 \cdot 1$
$$= 4 \cdot 9,$$

the same result as found by the straightforward method.

The saving in arithmetical work is illustrated by the following example where the marks are measured from 55 instead of 0.

Mark		Frequency	
X (Origin 0)	x (Origin 55)	f	fx
65	10	23	230
60	5	34	170
55	0	48	0
50	−5	29	−145
45	−10	16	−160
TOTALS		150	+400
			−305

$$\text{Sum of Marks} = \Sigma fx = 400 - 305$$
$$= 95$$

$$\text{Hence the Mean (with origin 55)} = \frac{95}{150}$$
$$= 0\cdot 63$$

$$\text{Mean (origin 0)} = 55 + 0\cdot 63 = 55\cdot 63$$

The symbolic representation of the calculation is $M = A + \dfrac{\Sigma fx}{N}$,

where A is the new origin, Σfx is the sum of the marks from the new origin and N is the number of marks.

Exercise

Take 6 and 4 as the origins for the calculation of the mean of the frequency distribution in Table 4. Establish that, no matter where the origin is selected, the answer is the same.

Mean from Frequency Distribution of Grouped Data

Class-intervals

The size of the class-interval is determined by the first and the last marks in the interval. For example, 5–9 is the group of five marks, 5, 6, 7, 8 and 9. It is advisable to make the limits of the interval inclusive. 0–9 indicates a range of ten marks from 0 to 9 inclusive.

When marks are grouped in class-intervals, it is assumed that the marks are scattered uniformly throughout the interval. In the example on page 12 there are seven marks in the interval 105–109. The actual numbers were 105, 106, 106, 109, 108, 105, 108, a total of 747. If it is assumed that the seven marks each have the value of the mid-mark in the interval, i.e. 107, the total would be 749 which is very little different from the actual total. When the entries in the class-intervals are fairly large, the difference may be very slight.

When the number of marks in the class interval is even the mid-value is between two marks. For example, the mid-value of the interval 0–9 is 4·5. A simple device for calculating the mid-value is to take the mean of the first and last marks of the interval. The mid-value of interval 10–19 is

$$\frac{10+19}{2} = \frac{29}{2}$$

$$= 14\cdot5.$$

The number of class-intervals in a distribution should generally lie between 10 and 20. If the distribution of marks ranges from 0 to 100, the size of the class interval could conveniently be 10. For I.Q.s, it is often convenient to take the intervals as 5 points of I.Q., i.e. 90–94, 95–99, 100–104, etc.

Calculation of Mean

Class-interval	Frequency
i	f
20–24	4
15–19	8
10–14	10
5–9	6
0–4	2
TOTAL	30

It is assumed in the above distribution that the 4 entries in the interval 20–24 are uniformly distributed and each may be taken as 22, giving a total of 88 marks. The sum of all the marks is thus obtained from the distribution:

X	f	fX
22	4	88
17	8	136
12	10	120
7	6	42
2	2	4
TOTALS	30	390

$$\text{Hence the mean} = \frac{390}{30}$$

$$= 13.$$

Changing Origin

The calculation may be simplified by changing the origin. If it is taken as 12, the distribution will read as follows:

x	f	fx
10	4	40
5	8	40
0	10	0
-5	6	-30
-10	2	-20
		$+80$
		-50
TOTALS	30	$+30$

$$\text{Mean (Origin 12)} = \frac{30}{30}$$

$$= 1$$

$$\text{Mean (Origin 0)} = 12 + 1$$

$$= 13.$$

Exercise

Take the origin as 7 in the above example and show that the result is the same.

No matter what origin is taken the result is the same. The nearer the origin is to the true mean, the simpler the calculation becomes. The selected origin is generally referred to as the assumed mean and is denoted by A.

Change of Unit

Further simplification of the manipulative calculation can be effected by another statistical device, to which reference was made in Chapter I, namely changing the unit. In the above calculation the origin was taken as 12 and the marks, as measured from 12 as origin, were -10, -5, 0, 5 and 10.

If, instead of units of 1, these marks were given in units of 5 they would become -2, -1, 0, 1 and 2. The transformations would be as follows:

X (Raw mark)	x (Origin 12)	d (Unit 5)
22	10	2
17	5	1
12	0	0
7	-5	-1
2	-10	-2

d is the deviation from the assumed mean in terms of a new unit. The calculation would proceed as follows:

f	d	fd
4	2	8
8	1	8
10	0	0
6	-1	-6
2	-2	-4
		16
		-10
TOTAL		$+6$

$$\text{Mean (Origin 12, unit 5)} = \frac{6}{30}$$

$$= 0 \cdot 2$$

$$\text{Mean (Origin 12, unit 1)} = 0{\cdot}2 \times 5$$
$$= 1$$
$$\text{Mean (Origin 0, unit 1)} = 12 + 1$$
$$= 13.$$

There is no need to go through each step in turn, as is shown in the following example:

(1) Class-interval	(2) Frequency	(3) Mid-point of interval	(4) Deviation from 24·5	(5) Deviation in unit of 10
i	f			d
0–9	6	4·5	−20	−2
10–19	8	14·5	−10	−1
20–29	10	24·5	0	0
30–39	4	34·5	+10	+1
40–49	2	44·5	+20	+2

The origin is taken at the largest frequency or as near to the mean as can be estimated; in the above case it would be at the interval 20–29. Hence the mid-point of this interval, namely 24·5, is taken as the origin. The mid-points of the class intervals below and above this are −20, −10, +10 and +20 respectively. The unit can now be changed to 10 thus giving the deviations as −2, −1, 0, +1 and +2 (column 5). The calculations are then as follows:

f	d	fd
6	−2	−12
8	−1	−8
10	0	0
4	+1	4
2	+2	4
		−20
		8
TOTALS 30		−12

$$\text{Mean score (Origin 24·5, unit 10)} = \frac{-12}{30}$$
$$= -0{\cdot}4$$

$$\text{Mean score (Origin 24·5, unit 1)} \begin{aligned} &= -0\!\cdot\!4 \times 10 \\ &= -4 \end{aligned}$$

$$\text{Mean score (Origin 0, unit 1)} \begin{aligned} &= 24\!\cdot\!5 + (-4) \\ &= 20\!\cdot\!5 \end{aligned}$$

The symbolic representation of these steps is:

$$M = A + \frac{\Sigma fd}{N} \times c,$$

where M is mean score, A is new origin (assumed mean), Σfd the sum of scores measured with A as the origin and in units of the size of the class-interval, N is the total number of marks, and c the size of the class-interval.

Exercises

The standardized scores in an arithmetic test and an English test produced the following distributions of marks:

English		Arithmetic	
100–104	1	100–104	0
95–99	1	95–99	2
90–94	0	90–94	0
85–89	1	85–89	4
80–84	3	80–84	1
75–79	0	75–79	3
70–74	4	70–74	5
65–69	7	65–69	3
60–64	6	60–64	5
55–59	3	55–59	4
50–54	0	50–54	1
45–49	4	45–49	1
40–44	2	40–44	4
35–39	2	35–39	1

Calculate the mean mark for each test.

Summary

The method of finding the mean from the three types of distributions are as follows:

Mean from List of Individual Marks

Mark
X

18
15
10
9
8
7
6
5
2
1
—
81
—

1. Find the sum of the marks:
$$\Sigma X = 81$$

2. Divide the sum of the marks (ΣX) by the number of marks (N):

$$N = \frac{\Sigma X}{N}$$

$$= \frac{81}{10}$$

$$= 8 \cdot 1.$$

Mean from Frequency Distribution of Individual Marks

Method 1

X	f	fX
10	1	10
9	3	27
8	4	32
7	4	28
6	5	30
5	5	25
4	3	12
3	2	6
2	2	4
1	1	1
TOTALS	30	175

Steps in Calculation

Step 1. Multiply each mark by its frequency to give fX: 10, 27 ...

Step 2. Add the figures in column fX to give the total sum of marks ΣfX:

$$\Sigma fX = 175$$

Step 3. Divide the sum of marks (ΣfX) by the number of marks (N):

$$N = \frac{\Sigma fX}{N}$$

$$= \frac{175}{30}$$

$$= 5 \cdot 83.$$

Method 2

Where marks and/or frequencies are large:

X	f	Deviation from 53 d	fd
56	1	+3	3
55	6	+2	12
54	8	+1	8
53	12	0	0
52	10	−1	−10
51	8	−2	−16
50	5	−3	−15
			+23
			−41
TOTALS	50		−18

Steps in Calculation

Step 1. Take assumed mean (new origin) near estimated mean; $A = 53$.

Step 2. In column *d* enter the deviation from the mean, paying attention to signs.

Step 3. Multiply the frequency (*f*) by the deviation from the mean (*d*) to give *fd*: 3, 12 ...

Step 4. Add the entries in column headed *fd*:
$$\Sigma fd = -18$$

Step 5. Divide the sum of the deviations (Σfd) by the total number of marks (*N*):
$$\frac{\Sigma fd}{N} = \frac{-18}{50} = -0\cdot36$$

Step 6. Add the assumed mean *A* to the mean of the deviation:
$$N = A + \frac{\Sigma fd}{N}$$
$$= 53 + (-0\cdot36)$$
$$= 52\cdot64.$$

Mean from Frequency Distribution of Grouped Data

i	*f*	Deviation from 102, unit 5 *d*	*fd*
130–134	2	+6	+12
125–129	3	+5	+15
120–124	3	+4	+12
115–119	8	+3	+24
110–114	8	+2	+16
105–109	16	+1	+16
100–104	20	0	0
95–99	14	−1	−14
90–94	10	−2	−20
85–89	6	−3	−18
80–84	5	−4	−20
75–79	4	−5	−20
70–74	1	−6	−6
			−98
			+95
TOTALS	100		−3

Steps in Calculation

Step 1. Choose assumed mean A at $A = 102$ (mid-point of interval 100–104); this becomes new origin.

Step 2. In column d enter deviations from mean in units of class-interval 5, paying regard to signs.

Step 3. Multiply frequency (f) by deviation (d) to give fd: 12, 15 ...

Step 4. Find Σfd: $\Sigma fd = -3$.

Step 5. Find the mean deviation by dividing Σfd by the total number of marks (N):

$$\frac{\Sigma fd}{N} = \frac{-3}{100}$$
$$= -0\cdot03$$

Step 6. Change the unit back to original unit:

$$\frac{\Sigma fd}{N} \times c = -0\cdot03 \times 5$$
$$= -0\cdot15$$

Step 7. Change the origin back to zero by adding the assumed mean:

$$M = A + \frac{\Sigma fd}{N} \times c$$
$$= 102 + (-0\cdot15)$$
$$= 101\cdot85.$$

Exercises

1. The frequency distribution of the I.Q.s of 688 pupils was as follows:

140–144	5
135–139	35
130–134	54
125–129	84
120–124	159
115–119	156
110–114	128
105–109	46
100–104	16
95–99	3
90–94	2

Calculate the mean I.Q. of the group.

2. The results of examinations in a County Transfer Test gave the following distributions of final marks.

100–104	20
95–99	62
90–94	126
85–89	223
80–84	244
75–79	175
70–74	42
65–69	18
60–64	1
55–59	1

Calculate the mean mark for the group.

3. In a County examination in English and arithmetic the distributions for each subject were as follows:

	English (frequency)	Arithmetic (frequency)
100–109	83	
90–99	203	
80–89	273	
70–79	300	19
60–69	297	276
50–59	292	474
40–49	280	504
30–39	263	385
20–29	196	315
10–19	145	278
0–9	71	145

Calculate mean mark for each subject.

CHAPTER V

The Scatter of Marks

A MARK has meaning only when its relationship with other marks is known; this was illustrated in Chapter II. Reference must be made to the standard of marking for which the mean is an appropriate measure.

Two sets of marks, even with the same mean, are not necessarily comparable. A difference in scatter gives different values to the marks in each set. The following sets of marks have the same mean:

Group A	Group B
117	130
116	121
115	115
113	114
112	111
110	111
109	108
108	106
106	104
104	90

The two sets of marks represent the results of an intelligence test given to two groups of pupils. The mean I.Q. of each group is 111. In group A, however, the I.Q.s tend to cluster about the mean, whereas in group B the spread of marks is greater, the individual differences in the group being larger.

Range

One measure of the scatter of marks is the range, i.e. the difference between the largest and the smallest values of the group. The range in group A is 117–104, i.e. 13, while in group B it is 130–90, i.e. 40.

The range takes into account only the extremes of the series; hence it is unreliable when frequent, or large, gaps occur in the distribution. For example, if two individuals having I.Q.s of 140 and 82 respectively were introduced into Group A the mean would not be altered, yet the range would now be 58 despite the fact that in the majority of cases the individuals of the group cluster round the mean more than in group B.

The range is used (1) when the data are too scanty or scrappy to justify the calculation of another measure of variation, and (2) when a knowledge of the total spread is all that is necessary.

Mean Deviation

To obtain a more accurate measure of the scatter, the amount by which each individual varies from the mean must be taken into consideration. In the previous example, the numerical value of the deviation of each I.Q. from the mean is as follows:

Group A	Group B
6	19
5	10
4	4
2	3
1	0
1	0
2	3
3	5
5	7
7	21
—	—
36	72
—	—

The mean deviations, ignoring signs, are 3·6 and 7·2 respectively. By this method the variation of group A is half that of group B, whereas by the method of the range, the variation of B was three times that of A. In the calculation of the *mean deviation* no account need be taken of the positive and negative aspect of the deviations.

Exercise

1. The marks scored by 34 children in the arithmetic test of a County Transfer examination were:

34	43	40	21	40	30	67
36	49	11	8	9	60	68
47	56	27	47	6	56	63
47	49	41	33	26	62	62
56	37	15	8	44	62	

Find (a) the mean mark, and (b) the mean deviation of the marks.

Standard Deviation

For reasons which are beyond the scope of this book to demonstrate, a method is adopted whereby the separate deviations are squared, the mean of these values found and finally the square root taken. The measure thus obtained is called the *standard deviation* and is the most important of all the measures of variation or dispersion. It is generally denoted by σ (the Greek letter sigma).

The calculation of σ is illustrated as follows:

Group A		Group B	
d	d^2	d	d^2
6	36	19	361
5	25	10	100
4	16	4	16
2	4	3	9
1	1	0	0
−1	1	0	0
−2	4	−3	9
−3	9	−5	25
−5	25	−7	49
−7	49	−21	441
	170		1010

$$\text{Mean } \frac{170}{10} = 17 \qquad\qquad \text{Mean } \frac{1010}{10} = 101$$

$$\sigma_A = \sqrt{17} = 4{\cdot}1 \qquad\qquad \sigma_B = \sqrt{101} = 10{\cdot}0$$

This method gives a measure which indicates that the scatter of group B is more than twice that of group A. The extreme deviations have considerable influence on the measure of variation when calculated in this manner, e.g. in group B the deviations 19 and −21 have a greater influence than in the calculation of mean deviation.

The standard deviation may be described as the square root of the mean of the squares of the deviations from the mean of the distribution, or, briefly, the root-mean-square deviation.

$$\sigma = \sqrt{\dfrac{\text{Sum of the squares of the deviations}}{N}}$$

$$= \sqrt{\dfrac{\Sigma(X-M)^2}{N}}$$

$$= \sqrt{\dfrac{\Sigma(x^2)}{N}} \quad \text{where } x = X - M$$

Exercise

Find the mean and standard deviation of the following ten marks:
67, 79, 75, 82, 78, 76, 60, 61, 59, 53

When the mean of the marks is a whole number the calculation of the standard deviation is relatively easy, but some simplification is desirable in other cases. The following simple example will illustrate:

X	d	d^2
7	1·8	3·24
6	0·8	0·64
5	−0·2	0·04
5	−0·2	0·04
3	−2·2	4·84

$$\Sigma X = 26 \qquad\qquad \Sigma d^2 = 8 \cdot 80$$

$$\text{Mean} = \frac{26}{5} \qquad\qquad \sigma^2 = \frac{\Sigma d^2}{N}$$

$$= 5 \cdot 2 \qquad\qquad\qquad = \frac{8 \cdot 80}{5}$$

$$= 1 \cdot 76$$

$$\therefore \quad \sigma = \sqrt{1 \cdot 76}$$

$$= 1 \cdot 33.$$

The calculation of the standard deviation can be made simpler by changing the origin. In the above example, the origin is selected as near the actual mean as can be estimated. In this instance, it would obviously be 5. The deviations and the squares become:

d	d^2
2	4
1	1
0	0
0	0
−2	4
$\Sigma d = 1$	$\Sigma d^2 = 9$

The standard deviation is not $\sqrt{\dfrac{\Sigma d^2}{N}}$ as the deviations d are from the assumed mean 5. It is:

$$\sigma = \sqrt{\left[\frac{\Sigma d^2}{N} - \left(\frac{\Sigma d}{N}\right)^2 \right]}.$$

This formula is proved in Appendix I.

$$\frac{\Sigma d}{N} = \frac{1}{5} \qquad\qquad \frac{\Sigma d^2}{N} = \frac{9}{5}$$
$$= 0.2 \qquad\qquad\qquad\quad = 1.8$$

$$\therefore \quad \left(\frac{\Sigma d}{N}\right)^2 = 0.04$$

$$\therefore \quad \sigma = \sqrt{(1.8 - 0.04)}$$
$$= \sqrt{1.76}$$
$$= 1.33$$

which is, of course, the same answer as by the previous method.

The following illustrates the calculation of standard deviation of a list of ten marks:

x	d	d^2
60	+5	25
58	+3	9
56	+1	1
55	0	0
55	0	0
51	−4	16
49	−6	36
48	−7	49
47	−8	64
45	−10	100
	+9	
	−35	
TOTALS	−26	300

$$N = 10 \qquad \Sigma d = -26 \qquad \Sigma d^2 = 300$$

$$\frac{\Sigma d}{N} = \frac{-26}{10} = -2 \cdot 6$$

$$\left(\frac{\Sigma d}{N}\right)^2 = (-2 \cdot 6)^2 = 6 \cdot 76$$

$$\frac{\Sigma d^2}{N} = \frac{300}{10} = 30$$

Method of Calculation

Step 1. Select one of the marks nearest to the estimated mean, e.g. $A = 55$.

Step 2. Find the deviations (d) from this mean, and find the algebraic total: $\Sigma d = -26$.

Step 3. Find the squares of the deviations (d^2), and find their total: $\Sigma d^2 = 300$.

Step 4. $\sigma^2 = \sqrt{\left[\dfrac{\Sigma d^2}{N} - \left(\dfrac{\Sigma d}{N}\right)^2\right]}$

$\qquad = \sqrt{(30 - 6 \cdot 76)}$

$\qquad = \sqrt{23 \cdot 24}$

$\therefore \quad \sigma = 4 \cdot 82.$

Standard Deviation of Frequency Distribution

To find the standard deviation of the frequency distribution given in Chapter IV, page 23, the steps follow the method outlined above but each deviation has to be multiplied by frequency.

X	f	d	fd	fd²
5	1	+2	+2	4
4	3	+1	+3	3
3	8	0	0	0
2	2	−1	−2	2
1	1	−2	−2	4
0	1	−3	−3	9
			+5	
			−7	
TOTALS	16		−2	22

$N = 16 \qquad \Sigma fd = -2 \qquad \Sigma fd^2 = 22$

$$\frac{\Sigma fd}{N} = \frac{-2}{16} = -0 \cdot 125$$

$$\left(\frac{\Sigma fd}{N}\right)^2 = (-0 \cdot 125)^2 = 0 \cdot 0156 \ldots \simeq 0 \cdot 02$$

$$\frac{\Sigma fd^2}{N} = \frac{22}{16} \simeq 1 \cdot 38$$

Method of Calculation

Step 1. Select an assumed mean: $A = 3$.

Step 2. Find the deviations (d) of each mark from the assumed mean.

Step 3. Multiply each deviation (d) by its respective frequency f, to give fd and find the total, paying attention to sign.

$$\Sigma fd = -2$$

Step 4. Square the deviations and multiply by the frequency f, to give fd^2. This is simply done by multiplying fd by d;

$$4, 3, 0, 2, 4, 9$$

Step 5. Find the total, i.e. Σfd^2.

Step 6. $\sigma^2 = \dfrac{\Sigma fd^2}{N} - \left(\dfrac{\Sigma fd}{N}\right)^2$

$\qquad = 1 \cdot 38 - 0 \cdot 02$

$\qquad = 1 \cdot 36$

$\therefore \quad \sigma = \sqrt{1 \cdot 36}$

$\qquad = 1 \cdot 17.$

Exercise

The marks for a class of 40 pupils gave the following frequency distributions. Calculate the standard deviation of the marks:

Mark	Frequency	Mark	Frequency
20	2	14	4
19	3	13	3
18	2	12	2
17	5	11	2
16	7	10	1
15	9		

Standard Deviation of Frequency Distribution of Grouped Data

The method follows a pattern similar to the previous example and is illustrated by the following distribution:

i	f	d	fd	fd^2
20–24	4	2	8	16
15–19	8	1	8	8
10–14	10	0	0	0
5–9	6	−1	−6	6
0–4	2	−2	−4	8
			+16	
			−10	
TOTALS	30		+6	38

$$N = 30 \qquad \Sigma fd = 6 \qquad \Sigma fd^2 = 38$$

$$\frac{\Sigma fd}{N} = \frac{6}{30}$$

$$= 0\cdot2$$

$$\left(\frac{\Sigma fd}{N}\right)^2 = 0\cdot04$$

$$\frac{\Sigma fd^2}{N} = \frac{38}{30}$$

$$\simeq 1\cdot27$$

Size of class-interval is 5

Method of Calculation

Step 1. Select an assumed mean e.g. $A = 12$, the mid-point of interval 10–14.

Step 2. Find the deviation from the mean but express this in units of the class-interval.

Step 3. Multiply each frequency f by its deviation d, to give fd;

$$8, 8, 0, -6, -4$$

Step 4. Find the product of the squares of the deviation and the frequencies to give fd^2; 16, 8, 0, 6, 8

Step 5. Find the total, i.e. $\Sigma fd^2 = 38$.

Step 6. Note the size of class-interval $c = 5$ as this is the unit in the calculation.

$$\sigma = \left\{ \sqrt{\left[\frac{\Sigma fd^2}{N} - \left(\frac{\Sigma fd}{N} \right)^2 \right]} \right\} \times c$$
$$= [\sqrt{(1\cdot27 - 0\cdot04)}] \times 5$$
$$= \sqrt{(1\cdot23)} \times 5$$
$$= 1\cdot11 \times 5$$
$$= 5\cdot55$$

Exercises

1. Calculate the standard deviation of the I.Q.s in the following distribution:

I.Q.	Frequency
135–139	2
130–134	5
125–129	14
120–124	40
115–119	40
110–114	35
105–109	23
100–104	26
95–99	10
90–94	1
85–89	1

2. Calculate the standard deviation of the marks in the following distribution:

Marks	Frequency
95–99	1
90–94	6
85–89	18
80–84	19
75–79	52
70–74	23
65–69	5
60–64	2
55–59	2

Sheets prepared in the following manner can be useful for calculating the means and standard deviation. They avoid the necessity of remembering the formula and also make the checking of the calculations easier.

Class	f	d	fd	fd^2
N		$+$		Σfd^2
		$-$		
		Σfd		

$c =$ $A =$

$\dfrac{\Sigma fd}{N} =$ $\left(\dfrac{\Sigma fd}{N}\right)^2 =$ $\dfrac{\Sigma fd^2}{N} =$

$$\text{MEAN} = A + \frac{\Sigma fd}{N} \times c \qquad\qquad \sigma = \left\{\sqrt{\left[\frac{\Sigma fd^2}{N} - \left(\frac{\Sigma fd}{N}\right)^{-}\right]}\right\} \times c$$

$= \boxed{}$ $= \boxed{}$

Exercises

Calculate the means and standard deviations of the following distributions:

1. Mark	Frequency	2. Mark	Frequency	3. I.Q.	Frequency
95–99	1	95–99	1	140–144	—
90–94	1	90–94	2	135–139	2
85–89	3	85–89	3	130–134	2
80–84	5	80–84	2	125–129	3
75–79	9	75–79	5	120–124	5
70–74	3	70–74	8	115–119	9
65–69	5	65–69	4	110–114	18
60–64	3	60–64	8	105–109	12
55–59	7	55–59	2	100–104	17
50–54	1	50–54	3	95–99	27
45–49	3	45–49	3	90–94	16
40–44	2	40–44	2	85–89	13
35–39	1	35–39	0	80–84	9
30–34	1	30–34	2	75–79	10
				70–74	7

4.	I.Q.	Frequency	5.	Mark	Frequency	6.	Mark	Frequency
	140–144	2		100–109	83		70–79	19
	135–139	3		90–99	203		60–69	276
	130–134	5		80–89	273		50–59	474
	125–129	6		70–79	300		40–49	504
	120–124	9		60–69	297		30–39	385
	115–119	21		50–59	292		20–29	315
	110–114	26		40–49	280		10–19	278
	105–109	17		30–39	263		0–9	145
	100–104	31		20–29	196			
	95–99	23		10–19	145			
	90–94	20		0–9	71			
	85–89	13						
	80–84	13						
	75–79	7						
	70–74	4						

CHAPTER VI

Comparison and Addition of Marks

THE following is an extract from a pupil's record card:

	Mark	Class average
English	68	58
History	70	52
Geography	70	52
French	65	50
Latin	70	66
Mathematics	90	60
Art	60	50

Clearly the mark 70 does not have the same meaning for each subject. The 70 in Latin appears to be a poorer mark than the 70 in history and in geography because the former is only 4 marks from the class average whereas the others are 18 from the class average. Do the 70's in history and geography have the same meaning? This question can be answered only if the scatter of marks is known.

Suppose the respective standard deviations for each subject are:

English	10	Latin	8
History	9	Mathematics	15
Geography	12	Art	5
French	10		

The marks in history and geography are both 18 above the class mean. In history this represents $\frac{18}{9}$, i.e. 2 standard deviations above the class average, whereas the geography mark is $\frac{18}{12}$, i.e. $1\frac{1}{2}$

standard deviations above the class average. It can therefore be concluded that the 70 in history is a better mark than the 70 in geography.

The 90 in mathematics is 30 above the class average, and as the standard deviation is 15, this is 2 deviations from the mean. In art the 60 is 2 standard deviations above the mean. It may be concluded, therefore, that the marks in mathematics and art represent the same relative standard of achievement. The 70 for Latin is only half a deviation above the mean whereas the 60 for art is 2 deviations above the mean; hence the art mark is a much better mark than the Latin one. Similarly, the geography and French marks represent the same level of attainment.

Marks cannot be compared or interpreted without reference to the mean and standard deviations.

Comparison of Marks

Suppose the pupil was asked to choose his three best marks. He would feel justified in selecting his marks in geography, Latin and mathematics, which would give a total of 230 marks $(70+70+90)$. History, art and mathematics would give him a total of 220 marks $(70+60+90)$. It has been shown that the history and art marks are respectively better than the geography and Latin marks. Hence the total of 220 marks (history, art and mathematics) represents a better performance than the 230 marks (geography, Latin and mathematics).

Raw marks cannot meaningfully be added without some adjustment which takes into account both the mean and standard deviation of each set of marks.

Exercises

1. Whis is the better mark: 70 (Mean, 60; σ, 8) or 67 (Mean, 55; σ, 9)?
2. Arrange the following marks in order of attainment: 75 (M, 60; σ, 12), 70 (M, 55; σ, 10), 68 (M, 48; σ, 15).

The value of the marks in the pupil's record card was determined by their distances from the mean measured in units of the standard deviation. The history mark was 2 standard deviations above the mean whereas the Latin mark was a $\frac{1}{2}$ deviation above the mean. These values, generally denoted by 2σ and 0.5σ respectively, are known as the standard scores.

Group tests of intelligence are generally standardized with a mean of 100 and a standard deviation of 15. Hence an I.Q. of 115 is 15 from the mean and is therefore equivalent to 1 deviation from the mean. Hence I.Q. 115 expressed as a standard score is 1σ.

A standard score of 2σ on a similar intelligence test is 2×15, i.e. 30, above the mean which is I.Q. 130. An I.Q. of 85 is 15 below the mean which is 1σ below the mean and is denoted by -1σ. -2σ is 30 below the mean I.Q., i.e. I.Q. 70.

Scores above the mean are positive whereas those below the mean are negative.

Exercise

Express as standard scores:

(a) I.Q.'s 120, 100, 70 and 95. (Mean, 100; σ, 15).
(b) Marks 40, 35, 50, 80 where the mean is 50; σ, 15.
(c) What I.Q.s are represented by 2σ, -1σ, -1.3σ, 1.7σ. (Mean I.Q. 100; σ, 15)?

The symbolic representation of the standard score is $\dfrac{X-M}{\sigma}$, where X = raw marks

M = Mean of marks

σ = Standard deviation of marks.

The idea of the standard scale may be illustrated as follows:

(1)	-3σ	-2σ	-1σ	0	$+1\sigma_A$	$+2\sigma$	$+3\sigma$	
(2)	55	70	85	100	115$_B$	130	145	Mean, 100; σ,15
(3)	20	30	40	50	60$_C$	70	80	Mean, 50; σ,10
(4)	20	35	50	65	80$_D$	95	110	Mean, 65; σ,15

The top line represents the standard scale. The second represents I.Q.s with mean 100 and standard deviation 15, and three sigma points above and below the mean. The two subsequent lines represent scales with means 50 and 65 and standard deviations 10 and 15 respectively.

Place on the Scale

The place of a mark on a scale is determined by its distance above or below the mean in terms of sigma units. For example 2σ is the point 2σ above the mean and on the respective scales is I.Q. 130, 70 and 95.

Conversion of Marks

A mark can be converted from any one scale to any other. For example, in the above diagram, it is clear that a mark of 40 on the third scale is equivalent to a mark of 50 on the fourth.

What is a mark of 65 on the third scale equivalent to on the fourth scale of marks? 65 is 15 marks above the mean which is 15/10, i.e. $1\cdot5\sigma$ as a standard score. $1\cdot5\sigma$ on the fourth scale is $1\cdot5 \times 15$, i.e. $22\cdot5$ above the mean 65 and yields a mark of $87\cdot5$ on scale 4. The respective positions on all four scales are denoted by A, B, C and D.

To convert X-marks (M_x, σ_x) to Y-marks (M_y, σ_y) the steps are as follows:

1. Find the difference between the X-mark and its mean, paying regard to sign:

$$X - M_x = 65 - 50$$
$$= 15$$

2. Express the difference in terms of the standard deviation and sigma distance from the mean by dividing the difference by the standard deviation, thus:

$$\frac{X - M_x}{\sigma_x} = \frac{15}{10}$$
$$= 1\cdot5$$

3. Convert the sigma distance from the mean into the actual distance from the Y-mean by multiplying by the standard deviation of the Y-marks:

$$\frac{X-M_x}{\sigma_x} \times \sigma_y = 1 \cdot 5 \times 15$$
$$= 22 \cdot 5$$

4. Add distance from Y-mean to the mean:

$$M_y + \frac{\sigma_y}{\sigma_x}(X-M_x)$$
$$= 65 + 22 \cdot 5$$
$$= 87 \cdot 5$$

Scaling

The complete operation of converting X-marks (M_x, σ_x) into Y-marks (M_y, σ_y) may be represented symbolically by the formula

$$Y = M_y + \frac{\sigma_y}{\sigma_x}(X-M_x)$$

This is known as the scaling equation.

Addition of Marks

The following table gives the teachers' estimates and the external examination marks scored by six pupils from a class.

Pupil	Estimate	Exam. mark	Total
B	82	68	150
S	80	70	150
M	78	72	150
O	50	55	105
P	40	49	89
E	36	62	98

The mean estimate of the whole class was 40 and the standard deviation 20, while the mean and standard deviation of the examination marks were 50 and 10, respectively.

When the estimates and marks are totalled, pupils B, S and M are equal followed in order by pupils O, E and P. The addition of raw marks is generally unsound and either both sets of marks should be converted to a common standard or one set of marks should be converted to the same standard as the other.

If the estimates are converted to the same scale as the examination marks and the marks then totalled the result is as follows:

Pupil	Estimate	σ Score	Estimates (mean, 50) (σ, 10)	Examination mark	Total
B	82	$2 \cdot 1\sigma$	71	68	139
S	80	$2\ \sigma$	70	70	140
M	78	$1 \cdot 9\sigma$	69	72	141
O	50	$0 \cdot 5\sigma$	55	55	110
P	40	$0\ \sigma$	50	49	99
E	36	$-0 \cdot 2\sigma$	48	62	110

The order has now been considerably changed and is M, S, B, O and E (equal) and P.

Graphical Method of Converting Marks

The equation for converting marks is $Y = M_y + \dfrac{\sigma_y}{\sigma_x}(X - M_x)$. This is represented graphically by a straight line and this can readily be drawn.

Suppose the line AB represents the conversion. To find the Y-mark Y_1, corresponding to the X-mark X_1, draw a horizontal line from Y_1 to meet AB at C. A line from C perpendicular to the X-axis will cut this axis at X_1. X_1 is the X-mark corresponding to Y_1.

The graph also provides a means of converting X-marks into Y-marks. The point D on the line AB is determined by drawing a vertical line from the point X_2. From D a horizontal line is drawn to meet the Y-axis at Y_2. This is the mark corresponding to X_2.

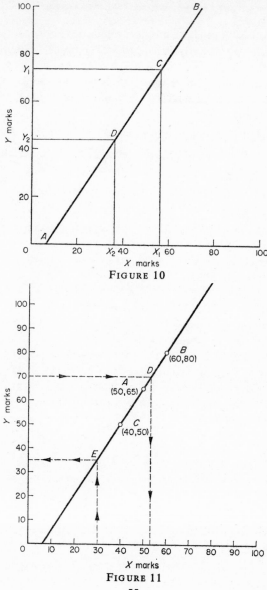

FIGURE 10

FIGURE 11

The method is illustrated by drawing a graph to convert a set of X-marks with mean, 50; σ, 10 into a set of Y-marks with mean, 65; σ, 15.

The straight line can be drawn by fixing two points on it, but greater confidence is achieved by using three easily determined points (see Figure 11).

1. Point A representing the means 50 and 65 (M_x, M_y).

2. Point B, representing one sigma distance above the mean $(M_x + \sigma_x)$ $(M_y + \sigma_y)$, i.e. $50 + 10 = 60$ and $65 + 15 = 80$.

3. Point C, representing one sigma distance below the mean $(M_x - \sigma_x)$ $(M_y - \sigma_y)$, i.e. 40, 50.

The line drawn through these three points gives the conversion graph.

To convert a Y-mark, e.g. 70, into its corresponding X-mark, draw a horizontal line through 70 on the Y-axis to meet the graph at D. From D draw a perpendicular to the X-axis; this line meets the X-axis at 53 which is the required X-mark.

Similarly an X-mark of 30 is converted into a Y-mark by drawing a vertical line at 30 to meet the line at E. From E a horizontal line is drawn to meet the Y-axis. This it does at 35. Hence an X-mark of 30 corresponds to a Y-mark of 35.

There is no need to draw the horizontal and vertical lines, the position on the graph can be determined by laying a ruler along the appropriate lines.

Exercise

1. Find the total of the estimates and marks in the example on page 53,
   (a) when the marks are converted to a scale with mean, 40 and σ, 20, and
   (b) when both estimates and marks are converted to a scale with mean, 40 and σ, 10.

2. The following table gives the marks of eight pupils who were being considered for scholarships on the basis of examinations in English and mathematics; the mean mark and standard deviation of all pupils who sat the examination were respectively $M_E = 40$, $\sigma_E = 10$ (English), $M_M = 50$ $\sigma_M = 20$ (mathematics).

Pupil	English	Mathematics
A	60	70
B	30	30
C	42	80
D	50	84
E	20	65
F	45	65
G	40	50
H	30	70

Find (a) the order of merit of the eight candidates when the raw marks are added; (b) the order of the combined marks when the standard of marking and the scatter of marks are made to be the same as the English mark by calculation; and (c) the order of the combined marks when the standard of marking and the scatter of marks are made to be the same as the mathematics marks by the graphical method.

CHAPTER VII

Percentiles

ANOTHER method of interpreting a pupil's mark is to indicate the percentage of pupils who score a lower mark. For example, 60 is an average mark if 50% of the pupils score less than 60 but 60 is a poor mark if 10% of the pupils have a mark of less than 60.

It is also important to know the level of ability or attainment of the group before the absolute value of a mark can be judged. 60 is a poor mark relative to the group examined if 10% of the group have lower marks, but nonetheless it may represent a high standard of attainment if the group examined are all highly intelligent. Norms can be fixed only when a complete age group is tested.

Percentile

The mark below which lies a certain percentage of marks is known as a percentile. For example, the 80th percentile is the mark below which lies 80% of marks.

This is denoted by P_{80}. Generally the xth percentile is denoted by P_x.

Percentile from List of Marks

The marks of twenty pupils are as follows:

90	50
85	50
80	48
78	45
75	40
62	36
60	32
60	30
60	30
54	25

Median

The mark below which 50% of the pupils lie is between 50 and 54 and is taken as the mark midway between them, i.e. 52. Hence the 50th percentile is 52. Therefore $P_{50} = 52$.

The 50th percentile, P_{50}, is called the *median*. Half of the marks in a distribution lie above the median and half below. If a distribution is skewed the median is sometimes used in preference to the mean.

Quartiles

P_{25}, the mark below which 25% of the class lie, is called the first or lower quartile and is denoted by the symbol Q_1. Five cases lie below P_{25} hence it lies between marks 40 and 36; we take $P_{25} = 38$.

Similarly, the 75th percentile, the third or upper quartile, Q_3, has 15 of the marks beneath it, and therefore lies between 62 and 75; hence $P_{75} = 68 \cdot 5$. The difference between Q_3 and Q_1 is known as the *interquartile range*.

$$Q_3 - Q_1 = 68 \cdot 5 - 38$$
$$= 40 \cdot 5$$

The interquartile range is sometimes used as a measure of the scatter of the marks and is preferred to the range since it takes into account all the marks and not merely the extremes.

Half the interquartile range is known as the *quartile deviation*.

$$Q = \frac{Q_3 - Q_1}{2}$$

Deciles

The percentiles $P_{10}, P_{20}, P_{30} \ldots P_{100}$ are known as the deciles. Two marks lie below P_{10} which is therefore 30, four marks below P_{20} which is therefore 34, six marks below P_{30} which is therefore $42 \cdot 5$.

Upper and Lower Limits

There is a difference between the statistical conception of a mark and a mark awarded in the classroom. A class average may be 53·5; there is, of course, no such mark. Fractional marks are a statistical concept based on the assumption that the marks are continuous lying on a scale ranging from 0 to the maximum mark.

DIAGRAM A

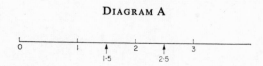

The mark of 2 has to be thought of as a quantity x such that $1·5 \leqq x \leqq 2·5$. Thus the lower limit is 1·5 and the upper limit is 2·5; similarly with class-intervals.

DIAGRAM B

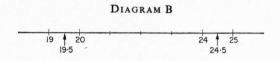

The interval 20–24 is regarded as having an upper limit of 24·5 and a lower limit of 19·5, i.e. such that $19·5 \leqq x \leqq 24·5$.

Exercise

86	50	27	17
84	45	26	12
73	37	24	9
62	31	20	5
58	29	18	3

From the above set of marks find the following percentiles:

P_{10}; P_{15}; P_{20}; P_{25}; P_{40}; P_{50}; P_{60}; P_{75}; P_{80}; P_{95}

Percentiles from a Frequency Distribution of Individual Marks

To calculate a percentile from a frequency distribution of individual marks, the cumulative frequency has first to be found. This gives the number of cases up to, but not including, each mark.

Mark	Frequency	Cumulative frequency
X	f	F
10	1	40
9	2	39
8	3	37
7	4	34
		—— P_{75}
6	5	30
5	8	25
4	7	17
		—— P_{25}
3	3	10
2	3	7
1	3	4
0	1	1
TOTAL	40	

In the above table column (3) is found by adding each frequency to the total of the frequencies below it. There is one pupil below 1, there are four pupils below 2, seven pupils below 3 and so on.

P_{25}, the 25th percentile, will be a mark below which 25%, i.e. 10, of the pupils lie. From the cumulative frequency this is 4, the lower limit of which is 3·5. Similarly P_{75} is the mark below which 75%, i.e. 30, of the pupils' marks lie. Again from column (3) this is 7 as 30 pupils have marks below 7; hence P_{75} is 6·5.

DIAGRAM C

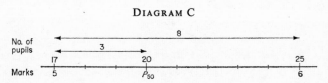

Twenty pupils have marks below P_{50}. Seventeen pupils have marks below 5 and twenty-five pupils have marks below 6; hence P_{50} lies between 5 and 6.

Three pupils (20–17) have marks between 5 and P_{50}, eight pupils (25–17) have marks between 5 and 6. Hence P_{50} lies $\frac{3}{8}$ of the way between 5 and 6. This distance is calculated from the lower limit of 5. Hence

$$P_{50} = 4\cdot5 + \frac{3}{8} \times 1$$
$$= 4\cdot5 + 0\cdot375$$
$$= 4\cdot875$$

Similarly P_{80} is the mark below which 80%, i.e. 32, pupils lie. This mark will lie somewhere between 7 and 8 between which there are four pupils. Beneath 7 there are 30 cases, hence P_{80} will lie $\frac{2}{4}$ of the way between 7 and 8.

$$P_{80} = 6\cdot5 + \frac{2}{4} \times 1$$
$$= 6\cdot5 + 0\cdot5$$
$$= 7$$

DIAGRAM D

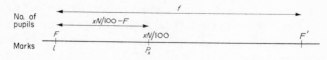

In general, $P_x = l + \dfrac{xN/100 - F}{F' - F}$

where N is the total number of entries,

    x is the percentage,

    l is the lower limit of the mark immediately below P_x,

    F is the cumulative frequency immediately below l,

    F' is the cumulative frequency immediately above l.

Exercise

Mark	f
10	3
9	4
8	7
7	9
6	3
5	6
4	4
3	2
2	1
1	1

From the above frequency distribution of marks, calculate the following percentiles:

$$P_5; P_{10}; P_{30}; P_{40}; P_{50}; P_{75}$$

Percentile from Frequency Distribution from Grouped Data

The calculation of a percentile is illustrated from the following frequency distribution.

i	f	F	
130–134	2	40	
125–129	0	38	
120–124	1	38	
115–119	3	37	
110–114	5	34	
			—— P_{75}
105–109	7	29	
100–104	6	22	
			—— P_{50}
95–99	2	16	
90–94	7	14	
85–89	5	7	
80–84	2	2	
TOTAL	40		

DIAGRAM E

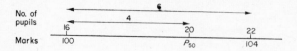

Sixteen pupils have marks below 100, hence four of the six pupils in the interval 100–104 lie below P_{50}. Hence P_{50} lies $\frac{4}{6}$ of the class interval above the lower limit of 100. Hence

$$P_{50} = 99 \cdot 5 + \frac{4}{6} \times 5$$
$$= 99 \cdot 5 + 3 \cdot 33$$
$$= 102 \cdot 83$$

P_{75} is the mark below which 30 scores lie and will be in the class-interval 110–114. It will be $\left(\frac{30-29}{5}\right)$ of the class-interval above the lower limit of 110.

$$P_{75} = 109 \cdot 5 + \frac{1}{5} \times 5$$
$$= 109 \cdot 5 + 1$$
$$= 110 \cdot 5$$

DIAGRAM F

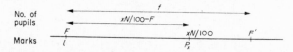

In general $P_x = l + \dfrac{xN/100 - F}{F' - F}$,

where l is the lower limit of the class-interval in which P_x falls,

N is the total frequency,

x is the percentage,

F is the cumulative frequency immediately below l,

F' is the cumulative frequency immediately above l.

Exercises

1. Calculate deciles and interquartile range for the following distributions:

I.Q.	f
130–134	2
125–129	3
120–124	3
115–119	8
110–114	8
105–109	16
100–104	20
95–99	14
90–94	10
85–89	6
80–84	5
75–79	4
70–74	1
	100

2. Calculate P_{15}; P_{25}; P_{50}; P_{75} and P_{85} for the following distributions

I.Q.	f
100–104	20
95–99	62
90–94	126
85–89	223
80–84	244
75–79	175
70–74	42
65–69	18
60–64	1
55–59	1

Graphical Method of Calculating Percentile

(a) Frequency Distribution of Individual Marks

The cumulative frequency gives the number of pupils whose score does not exceed each mark. The cumulative frequency can be expressed as a percentage of the total marks as given in column 3, Table 4.

3*

TABLE 4

Mark	Frequency	Cumulative frequency	% Frequency
10	1	40	100
9	2	39	97·5
8	3	37	92·5
7	4	35	82·5
6	5	30	75·0
5	8	25	62·5
4	7	17	42·5
3	3	10	25·0
2	3	7	17·5
1	3	4	10·0
0	1	1	2·5

If these percentages are plotted against their marks as in Figure 12, any percentile can be read from the graph.

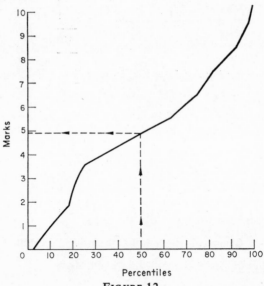

Percentiles

FIGURE 12

For example, P_{50} is found by finding the point on the graph where a vertical line from 50% meets the curve and drawing a horizontal line from this point to the Marks axis. It cuts it at the point 4·8, hence $P_{50} = 4·8$. This corresponds to the calculation (page 62) which gave 4·875.

Exercises

Find by the graphical method the deciles and quartile deviation of the following distributions.

Mark	
12	2
11	6
10	5
9	3
8	3
7	5
6	4
5	2
4	2
3	2
2	0
1	1
	35

Check the answers by calculation.

(b) Frequency Distribution of Grouped Data

The method is similar to that for individual marks and is illustrated by the data in Table 5.

TABLE 5

i	f	F	$\%F$
130–134	1	40	100
125–129	2	39	97·5
120–124	3	37	92·5
115–119	4	34	85·0
110–114	11	30	75·0
105–109	8	19	47·5
110–104	4	11	27·5
95–99	3	7	17·5
90–94	2	4	10·0
85–89	1	2	5·0
80–84	1	1	2·5

The percentage cumulative frequency is calculated and plotted against the upper limit of each class interval (Figure 13):

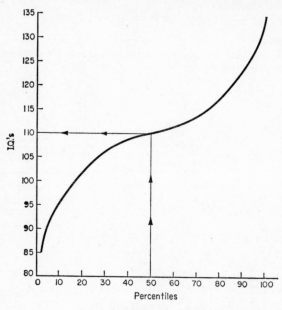

FIGURE 13

The percentiles are read in the usual manner. For example, P_{50} will be 110. Calculations show that P_{50} is 109·94.

Exercise

From Figure 13 read off the deciles and check your results by calculation.

Graphical Method of Scaling Marks by Use of Percentile Curves

It has been shown that marks can be regarded as equivalent if their sigma distances above or below their respective means are the same. Thus 60 from a distribution with mean 50 and σ10 is equivalent to 80 from a distribution with mean, 65 and σ, 15.

Another method would be to regard as equivalent marks with the same percentile rank. Thus in a distribution if P_{50} was 50 and, in another, P_{50} was 60, the two marks could be regarded as equivalent.

Consider the distributions in columns (1) and (4) of Table 6.

TABLE 6

Interval	f_A	F_A	$\%F_A$	f_B	F_B	$\%F_B$
95–99	1	50	100			
90–94	2	49	98			
85–89	4	47	94	1	50	100
80–84	3	43	86	5	49	98
75–79	4	40	80	3	44	88
70–74	6	36	72	5	41	82
65–69	4	30	60	5	36	72
60–64	6	26	52	12	31	62
55–59	5	20	40	8	19	38
50–54	5	15	30	5	11	22
45–49	3	10	20	4	6	12
40–44	4	7	14	1	2	4
35–39	2	3	6	1	1	2
30–34	1	1	2			

The percentage cumulative frequencies shown in columns (3) and (6) are plotted and their curves drawn on the same graph (Figure 14):

Graphs A and B represent percentage cumulative frequency curves of the distributions A and B respectively.

To convert a mark of 81 on scale A to scale B draw a horizontal line from 81 on the vertical axis to meet graph A at P. From P draw a vertical line to meet graph B at point Q. This point is at the same percentile on curve B as P is on A. From this point Q draw a horizontal line to meet the marks-axis; so 74 is the converted mark.

To scale B marks to the same scale as A, a similar procedure is followed starting with a horizontal line from the marks-axis and meeting first the B curve.

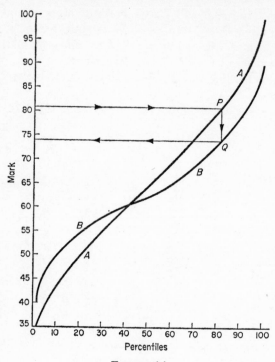

FIGURE 14

Table 7 gives a series of marks converting from *A* to *B* and from *B* to *A*.

TABLE 7

Raw mark A	Scaled on B	Raw mark B	Scaled on A
81	74	76	82
73	68	84	93
61	61	69	74
55	57	55	51
49	53	42	35

Exercises

1.

i	
90–94	1
85–89	4
80–84	7
75–79	6
70–74	3
65–69	5
60–64	5
55–59	4
50–54	2
45–49	2
40–44	1

From the above frequency distribution calculate the following percentiles and check the results by graphical method.

$P_{10}; P_{20}; P_{30}; P_{40}; P_{50}; P_{60}; P_{70}; P_{80}; P_{90}.$

2.

i	f
70–79	19
60–69	276
50–59	474
40–49	504
30–39	385
20–29	315
10–19	278
0–9	145

From the above frequency distributions calculate $P_{25}; P_{50}; P_{75}$. Check the results by graphical method.

CHAPTER VIII

The Normal Curve

IMAGINE a large number of men assembled and lined up according to height, with men of the same height standing behind one another. At and near the middle of the row, where men of average height stand, the files extend far to the rear, while near the ends of the row, where the small and the tall men stand, the files are short. At the extreme ends some of the men may have no one behind them. The view of the files from a helicopter immediately above the assembly would appear as in Figure 15.

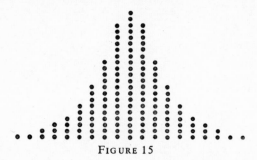

FIGURE 15

Most of the diagrammatic representations of frequency distributions of marks tend to have this general form—the measures are greatest round the centre and taper off from the highest point or the crest equally to right and left. The curve drawn through the points representing the frequency values is perfectly symmetrical about a perpendicular dropped from the highest point of the curve to the base line (see Figure 16); it is known as the normal curve.

The normal frequency curve is of great importance in educational statistics. It represents approximately the distribution of mental capacity among primary school pupils and has many important educational implications.

Individual Differences

One of the greatest advances in education has been to recognise individual differences and the need to adjust education to the mental capacity of each child. While there are very great differences in capacity between individuals, there is a continuity which ranges from one end of the scale to the other. In a school or class where the pupils are not specially selected there is a continuous range of intelligence from the weakest intellect to the strongest; there is no sudden demarcation of the mental defective from the superior intelligence. There is a danger in the use of categories such as defective, genius, able pupils and dull and backward: there is a continuity over all the classes, the one merging into the other. Similarly with examination marks; there is little or no difference between the attainments of pupils whose marks are close together.

Departures from Normality

There are some points which must be clearly understood about the normal curve:

(1) If the number of entries is small there may be discontinuity as is shown in Figure 3 (page 13). The results of a single class seldom give a normal curve. The greater the size of the group, however, the more nearly normal does the curve become. The frequency distribution of I.Q.s of a class, or even a school, cannot be expected to produce a normal curve. On the other hand, when the results from several schools are combined the distribution more nearly approaches normality.

(2) If the sample of pupils being tested is not itself normal in character and the examination is not specially designed, the frequency distribution will not produce a normal curve. If a class of dull and backward children is tested by an examination

intended for normal pupils of a similar age the results will not be normal.

(3) Departures from normality may be due to the nature of the examination or to the nature of the group tested. An examination, however, can be constructed to produce a normal curve even with a group which itself is not normal. Many teachers do not realize that examinations can be constructed to produce a distribution of marks in a variety of forms.

Sections under Normal Curve

Since the normal curve can be defined accurately in mathematical terms, many interesting and useful calculations can be made from it. For example, it is obvious that a perpendicular line drawn from the mid point of the base to the crest of the curve will divide the area under the curve into two equal portions. 50% of the group lies above the mean and 50% below the mean (see Figure 16).

A Table has been constructed (see Appendix II) to show the area under the normal curve between the mean and the various sigma distances from the mean expressed as a proportion of the total area.

The percentage of cases lying between the mean and $+1\sigma$ is 34·13 (in the Table the figure is 0·3413). This is true whatever the value of sigma provided the distribution is approximately normal. When converted into an actual scale this means, for example, that 34% of the pupils lie between I.Q. 100 and I.Q. 115, when the mean I.Q. is 100 and σ is 15. When the mean mark is 65 and σ is 15, 34% of the distribution lies between 65 and 80. Similarly, 34·13% of the cases in a normal distribution lie between I.Q. 100 and I.Q. 85, that is between 0 and -1σ. Therefore, between I.Q. 85 and I.Q. 115 lies 68·26% of the population (see Figure 17).

Similarly in a normal distribution a set of marks with mean, 50 and σ, 10, 68·26% of the marks lie between 40 and 60.

Figure 18 shows how to calculate the percentage of the population which lies between I.Q. 110 and I.Q. 120 (M 100, σ15).

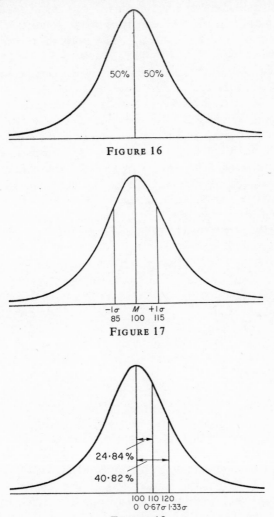

FIGURE 16

FIGURE 17

FIGURE 18

I.Q. 110 is 0.67σ above the mean. In Appendix II the proportion of cases between the mean and $.67\sigma$ is $.2486$, hence 24.86% of the population lies between I.Q. 100 and I.Q. 110. As I.Q. 120 is 1.33σ above mean I.Q. 100, the proportion of the population between the mean and I.Q. 120 is 40.82%. Therefore, the proportion between I.Q. 110 and I.Q. 120 is $40.82 - 24.86$, i.e. 15.96%, say 16%. All such calculations are valid only when the population is normally distributed.

Calculations can be done in the reverse way. Given a percentage of the population it is possible to calculate the limits of I.Q. containing this percentage. For example, the middle 50% is bounded by an I.Q. which cuts off 25% above the mean and 25% below the mean. The table in Appendix II shows that the line drawn through $+0.67\sigma$ cuts off 25% of the area to the right of the mean. Since σ is 15, 0.67σ represents 10.05 (0.67×15) points of I.Q. and hence this I.Q. is 110. The limits, therefore, of the middle 50% are 90 to 110 I.Q. (see Figure 19).

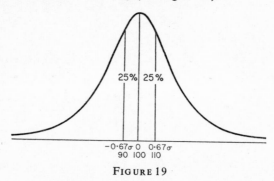

$$-0.67\sigma \quad 0 \quad 0.67\sigma$$
$$90 \quad 100 \quad 110$$

FIGURE 19

It was suggested that the 'O' grade of the Scottish Certificate of Education should be within reach of all pupils (even the weakest) who are in the top 30% of the ability range, i.e. pupils who are 20% from the mean. Twenty per cent is cut off at 0.52σ from the mean, which in terms of I.Q. is 7.8, hence the weakest pupil likely to pass will have an I.Q. of approximately 108.

The illustrations which have been given have referred mainly to I.Q.s but calculations can be made for any mean and standard deviation. Take, for example, a normal distribution with mean, 12 and σ, 4; what percentage of cases (a) falls between the marks 8 and 16, (b) lie above 18, and (c) lie below 6?

(a) Marks of 8 and 16 lie between -1σ and $+1\sigma$, that is, there is a proportion of 34·13 cases above the mean and 34·13 below; hence the marks 8 and 16 include 68·26% of the population.

(b) A mark of 18 is 6 points above the mean, that is at 1·5σ. The percentage of cases between the mean and 1·5σ is 43·32; hence the percentage of cases above this point is 6·68.

(c) Similarly, below 6 there is, approximately 7% of the total, group.

Approximation

In some of the examples a mark or I.Q. is given which is not a whole number, e.g. I.Q. 110·05. Such accuracy may be arithmetically justifiable, but educational measurement does not warrant such refinement. Individual marks should normally be expressed as whole numbers.

Exercises

1. Given a normal distribution, mean, 29, σ, 4·5, what percentage of the distribution lies between 20 and 38?
2. In a normal distribution the mean is 14·5 and σ, 2·5, what percentage of the group lies (a) between 12 and 16, (b) above 18, and (c) below 10?
3. In a normal distribution with mean, 65 and σ, 15 what marks cut off the (a) top 25·14%, (b) middle 30·34% and (c) bottom 20% of the distribution?
4. Assuming a normal distribution of I.Q. mean, 100 σ, 15, (a) what percentage lies above I.Q. 110, and (b) what I.Q.s enclose the middle 40%?

Influence of Scatter

The normal curve although always symmetrical can vary in its form. It may be contracted or spread out, depending on the scatter of marks. Figure 20 shows two normal curves which have the same mean, but differ in scatter. These distributions, for example, could represent the distribution of intelligence of equal numbers of boys and girls; the distribution of I.Q.s of the boys has a bigger scatter than that of the girls.

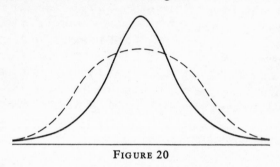

FIGURE 20

Drawing the Normal Curve

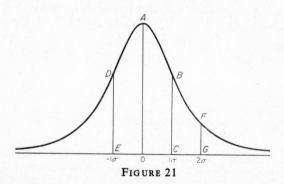

FIGURE 21

The first step is to determine the maximum height of the curve, AO in Figure 21.

The lines drawn from a point on the curve perpendicular to the base line are known as ordinates. AO is denoted by y_0 and is termed the mean ordinate.

All the other ordinates are a fixed proportion of y_0. For example, the ordinate BC at $+1\sigma$ from the mean, denoted by y_σ is approximately 61% of the size of y_0. DE at -1σ, denoted by $y_{-\sigma}$ is the same size. FG, the ordinate at $+2\sigma$, denoted by $y_{2\sigma}$, is approximately 13·5% of the size of y_0.

By drawing a sufficient number of ordinates the curve can be readily sketched. This is best done on graph paper, on which it is not necessary to draw the ordinates but merely to plot the points at the top of the ordinates which lie on the curve.

Thirteen points are sufficient to give a good indication of the curve. They are as follows:

$$\text{Assume } y_0 = 100$$
$$\text{at } 0.5\sigma, \ y_{0\cdot5\sigma} = 88\cdot25$$
$$\text{at } 1\sigma, \ y_\sigma = 60\cdot65$$
$$\text{at } 1.5\sigma, \ y_{1\cdot5\sigma} = 32\cdot47$$
$$\text{at } 2\sigma, \ y_{2\sigma} = 13\cdot53$$
$$\text{at } 2.5\sigma, \ y_{2\cdot5\sigma} = 4\cdot39$$
$$\text{at } 3\sigma, \ y_{3\sigma} = 1\cdot11$$

The ordinates for negative σ values are identical to those for positive values.

The heights of the ordinates for all σ values are given in Appendix III. For example, the ordinate at 1.26σ is $0.4521\ y_0$ and an ordinate which is $0.13\ y_0$ is at 2.02σ. Intermediate values are calculated by proportion. For example, an ordinate which is $0.25\ y_0$ is at 1.665σ, because

$$0.2521 \text{ is at } 1.66\sigma$$
$$\text{and } \quad 0.2480 \text{ is at } 1.67\sigma$$
$$\therefore \quad 0.0041 \text{ accounts for } -0.01\sigma$$
$$\therefore \quad 0.0021 \text{ accounts for } -0.005\sigma$$
$$\therefore \quad 0.2500 \text{ is at } 1.665\sigma$$

Exercises

1. What proportion of the mean ordinate under a normal curve are those at (1) 1.22σ, (2) -0.5σ, (3) 2.85σ, (4) 1.325σ?

2. At what σ point from the mean are the ordinates which are the following percentages of the mean ordinate:

$$82\%, \ 65.5\%, \ 40.2\%, \ 20\%, \ 3.55\%?$$

To Draw a Normal Curve with Given Standard Deviation

(a) With Frequency Distribution of Individual Marks

The height of the mean ordinate is given by the formula

$$y_0 = \frac{N}{\sigma\sqrt{(2\pi)}}$$

Where N is the number of cases,
  σ is the standard deviation,
$\sqrt{(2\pi)}$ is 2·51.

Suppose there are 100 cases and $\sigma = 10$

$$\text{Then } y_0 = \frac{100}{10 \times 2\cdot51} = 3\cdot98$$

Hence $y_{0\cdot5\sigma} = 0\cdot8825 \times 3\cdot98 = 3\cdot51$
  $y_\sigma = 0\cdot6065 \times 3\cdot98 = 2\cdot41$
  $y_{1\cdot5\sigma} = 0\cdot3247 \times 3\cdot98 = 1\cdot29$
  $y_{2\sigma} = 0\cdot1353 \times 3\cdot98 = 0\cdot54$
  $y_{2\cdot5\sigma} = 0\cdot0439 \times 3\cdot98 = 0\cdot17$
  $y_{3\sigma} = 0\cdot0111 \times 3\cdot98 = 0\cdot04$

The normal curve can be drawn as in Figure 22.

(b) With Frequency Distribution of Grouped Data

In this instance the height of the mean ordinate is given by the formula

$$y_0 = \frac{Nc}{\sigma\sqrt{(2\pi)}},$$

where N is the number of cases,
  c is the size of class interval,
  σ is the standard deviation
$\sqrt{(2\pi)}$ is 2·51.

We draw the normal curve for the frequency distribution in Table 8 as follows:

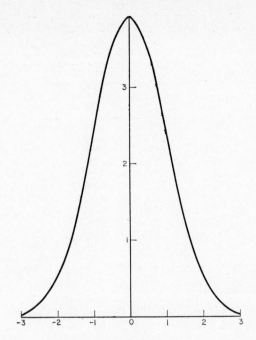

FIGURE 22

TABLE 8

90–94	1
85–89	2
80–84	3
75–79	5
70–74	8
65–69	11
60–64	12
55–59	10
50–54	9
45–49	5
40–44	3
35–39	1
TOTAL	70

The mean of this distribution is 62·71, and σ is 11·7. The steps needed to find the appropriate ordinates are shown in Table 9.

TABLE 9

Class-interval (1)	Mid point of class interval (2)	σ distance from mean (3)	Proportion of mean ord. (4)	Theoretical frequency (5)	Observed frequency (6)
90–94	92	2·503	·0439	·523	1
85–89	87	2·076	·1150	1·37	2
80–84	82	1·648	·2563	3·055	3
75–79	77	1·221	·4751	5·662	5
70–74	72	·794	·7319	8·723	8
65–69	67	·367	·9338	11·13	11
60–64	62	·006	1·0	11·918	12
55–59	57	−·488	·8869	10·57	10
50–54	52	−·915	·655	7·81	9
45–49	47	−1·343	·4075	4·857	5
40–44	42	−1·77	·2088	2·489	3
35–39	37	−2·197	·0889	1·06	1

Method of Calculation

Step 1.
(Column 2)
Write down the mid point of each class interval, e.g. 92, 87...

Step 2.
(Column 3)
Calculate the σ distance from the mean of each of the mid points, e.g. 92 is

$$\frac{92-62\cdot71}{11\cdot7}=2\cdot503$$

Step 3.
(Column 4)
Find from Appendix III the proportion of the mean ordinates of each ordinate at the σ distance in column 3 from the mean, e.g. 2·503σ is 0·0439.

Step 4.
Find the height of the mean ordinate.

$$y_0 = \frac{Nc}{\sigma\sqrt{(2\pi)}}$$
$$= \frac{70\times5}{11\cdot7\times2\cdot51}$$
$$= 11\cdot92$$

Step 5.   Calculate the height of each ordinate, e.g.

(Column 5) $y_{2 \cdot 503} = 0 \cdot 0439 y_0$

                       $= 0 \cdot 0439 \times 11 \cdot 92$

                       $= 0 \cdot 523$

Step 6.   Draw on graph paper a base line with mean at 0 and
                the σ distance from the mean 2·503, 2·076, etc. Plot
                the points 0·523, 1·370, etc. above the appropriate σ
                distances. Sketch in the curve (Figure 23).

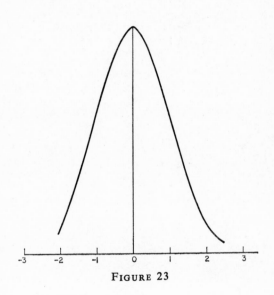

FIGURE 23

A comparison of the frequencies in columns 5 and 6 gives an
indication of the extent to which the observed frequency approxi-
mates to a normal distribution.

Exercises

1. Draw on the same graph the normal curves with σ, 20, N, 100, and with σ, 10, N, 100.

2. Calculate the theoretical frequencies to give a normal curve from the following distribution:

i	f
65–69	1
60–64	2
55–59	2
50–54	5
45–49	11
40–44	7
35–39	6
30–34	3
25–29	1
20–24	1
15–19	1

CHAPTER IX

Correlation

IT IS sometimes important to know how one set of marks is related to another set. If the I.Q.s of a class have little or no relationship with the pupils' marks in arithmetic, the teacher may wonder whether her teaching of arithmetic is sound. There are several other conclusions which may be drawn. For example, the I.Q.s may not be good assessments or the arithmetic test may have been a faulty one. Any conclusion would require further investigation, but it is essential in the first instance to have some measure of the relationship.

The relationship between marks at one stage of education with those at another is very important. Primary school marks are used to predict the possible success of a pupil in secondary education and, if there is no relationship, pupils may as well be transferred without any advice from the primary school teacher. Again, the relationship between marks in the secondary school and those gained at university is important, because prospective students are selected on the assumption that those who do well in the secondary school will do well at university.

Correlation Coefficient

The measure of the relationship between marks is known as the correlation coefficient and is denoted by r (see p. 91) or in certain instances by ρ (rho) (see p. 90).

If ten pupils were given a verbal reasoning test and an examination in English, and the order of merit of the I.Q.s was the same as the English marks the correlation would be perfect. The relative position of each pupil is the same in one test as in the other: there is a one-to-one correspondence between the two sets of results. In such instances the correlation coefficient ρ is 1. When r is 1 the predictive value of any one set of marks as regards the other is 100%: the pupil who is tenth in the verbal reasoning test will be tenth in the English test.

Suppose the pupils' English marks were compared with their heights: since there is no relationship between them r would be 0. Predicting one from the other would be no better than guesswork since there is no correspondence or correlation between the two sets of figures.

Between the limits of 1 and 0 there are relationships of varying degrees expressed by coefficients such as 0·3, 0·6, 0·7 or any other decimal between 0 and 1. For example, the relationship between height and weight is not perfect nor is it zero: there are small heavy men and tall light men. The degree of accuracy with which one set of values can be predicted from the other depends on the size of correlation coefficient. The correlation between I.Q.s and school marks generally does not exceed 0·75 as there are too many interference factors such as home conditions, perseverance and interest.

If by some curious chance one set of marks was in exactly the reverse order from another the correlation coefficient would be −1. Prediction again would be 100% accurate.

Coefficients thus range from −1 to 1 and the correlation may be thought of as distributed along a scale extending from −1 to 1. Great care must be taken in the interpretation of a correlation coefficient, and, generally, other measurements must be made before a decision is reached as to the extent of the correlation. In educational measurements there are many sources of error due to the variability of human beings and the relative crudity of the measuring instruments. The following gives a rough indication of the degree of the relationship between measures:

0·00 to 0·20 negligible
0·20 to 0·40 low
0·40 to 0·60 moderate
0·60 to 0·80 substantial
0·80 to 1·00 high

Ranks

Table 10 gives a list of I.Q.s and the corresponding marks for the same pupils in an English examination.

TABLE 10

Pupil	I.Q.	English mark
A	142	80
B	133	67
C	130	83
D	130	76
E	128	76
F	128	78
G	128	65
H	128	73
I	125	53
J	122	59
K	121	49
L	119	50
M	118	54
N	117	49
O	115	59
P	113	62
Q	109	59
R	106	57
S	106	40
T	92	28

To find the relationship between the two sets of measures, the order of merit of the pupils in each list must be compared. Each pupil is allotted a rank which indicates his position when the series is arranged in descending order of magnitude.

For I.Q. pupils A and B are given ranks 1 and 2, respectively. Pupils C and D are equal and the method of allocating a rank is to give each pupil the average of the ranks that would have been occupied by those tying, as if they had been forced to occupy consecutive ranks by being placed in alphabetical order within the group. Pupils C and D would have been placed third and fourth, hence each is given the rank $\frac{1}{2}(3+4)$, i.e. $3\frac{1}{2}$ or 3·5. Pupils E, F, G and H would have been placed fifth, sixth, seventh and eighth, hence each is given the rank $\frac{1}{4}(5+6+7+8)$, i.e. $6\frac{1}{2}$ or 6·5. The respective ranks for I.Q. are, therefore, 1, 2, 3·5, 3·5, 6·5, 6·5, 6·5, 6·5, 9, 10, 11, 12, 13, 14, 15, 16, 17, 18·5, 18·5, 20.

Arranging a list of marks in order can be troublesome, but the following method simplifies the working:

(a) Write down class intervals which include the highest and lowest mark:

80–89
70–79
60–69
50–59
40–49
30–39
20–29

(b) Starting with the first pupil, enter each mark in the appropriate interval:

80–89	80		83					
70–79			73		76	76		78
60–69	62	65	67					
50–59	50	53	54		57	59	59	59
40–49	40					49	49	
30–39								
20–29			28					

(c) The marks can now be readily written in order:

83, 80, 78, 76, 76, 73, 67, 65, 62, 59, 59, 59, 57, 54, 53, 50, 49, 49, 40, 28.

(d) The ranks are:

1, 2, 3, 4·5, 4·5, 6, 7, 8, 9, 11, 11, 11, 13, 14, 15, 16, 17·5, 17·5, 19, 20.

Rank Correlation Coefficient

The calculation of the rank correlation coefficient, denoted by ρ, is shown as follows:

I.Q. rank	English rank	D	D^2
1	2	−1	1
2	7	−5	25
3·5	1	2·5	6·25
3·5	4·5	−1	1
6·5	4·5	2	4
6·5	3	3·5	12·25
6·5	8	−1·5	2·25
6·5	6	0·5	0·25
9	15	−6	36
10	11	−1	1
11	17·5	−6·5	42·25
12	16	−4	16
13	14	−1	1
14	17·5	−3·5	12·25
15	11	4	16
16	9	7	49
17	11	6	36
18·5	13	5·5	30·25
18·5	19	−0·5	0·25
20	20	0	0
		Total	292·00

Steps in Calculating ρ

Step 1. Rank the measures in order of size.

Step 2. Subtract the rank of each measure in the second series from its corresponding rank in the first series. The differences are denoted by D, i.e. −1, −5, 2·5 ...

Step 3. Square each of these differences to give D^2, i.e. 1, 25, 6·25 ...

Step 4. Find the sum $\Sigma D^2 = 292$.

4

Step 5. Use the formula $\rho = 1 - \dfrac{6\Sigma D^2}{N(N^2-1)}$ (where N is the number of pupils)

$$N = 20. \qquad \rho = 1 - \frac{6 \times 292}{20(400-1)}$$

$$= 1 - \frac{1752}{7980}$$

$$= 1 - 0\cdot 22$$

$$= 0\cdot 78$$

It can be concluded, therefore, that there is a high relationship between the I.Q. and the English marks. Column D shows the discrepancies in the orders. The largest difference is that of pupil P whose I.Q. was 113 and whose English mark was 62, and further investigation would be required to find a reason for this difference.

The following points are worth noting:

(a) the sign of D makes no difference to the calculation as D^2 is always positive.

(b) a simple rule for calculating the square of a number such as $6\cdot 5$ is to take the next highest number, i.e. 7, multiply by the figure before the decimal point, which is 6 and add $0\cdot 25$ $(6 \times 7 + 0\cdot 25 = 42\cdot 25)$.   Similarly, $3\cdot 5^2 = 3 \times 4 + 0\cdot 25 = 12\cdot 25$.

(c) $N^2-1 = (N+1)(N-1)$, hence the denominator $N(N^2-1)$ is really written as a product of factors, e.g. for $N = 27$, the denominator is $27 \times 28 \times 26$.

The rank correlation method is suitable for fairly small numbers up to about 30.

Exercises

1. Find the correlation coefficient ρ between the teacher's estimates in English and English test scores of twenty pupils.

Pupil	Estimate	Mark		Pupil	Estimate	Mark
A	88	89		K	92	94
B	95	96		L	84	82
C	97	92		M	77	74
D	82	83		N	54	55
E	93	84		O	75	71
F	86	82		P	60	56
G	87	84		Q	45	47
H	94	92		R	48	51
I	83	83		S	40	39
J	81	73		T	69	68

2. Find the correlation coefficient between the English and arithmetic marks of the following twenty pupils.

Pupil	English mark	Arith. mark		Pupil	English mark	Arith. mark
A	73	74		K	80	79
B	78	80		L	87	76
C	96	78		M	77	84
D	79	79		N	69	67
E	90	90		O	69	73
F	79	87		P	65	75
G	81	71		Q	63	40
H	87	99		R	60	63
I	88	90		S	59	46
J	82	86		T	53	60

What is the degree of relationship between the two sets of marks?
Which three pupils show the greatest divergence in the respective orders of merit?

Product-Moment Coefficient of Correlation

The general product-moment formula for a correlation coefficient is given by

$$r = \frac{\Sigma xy}{\sqrt{(\Sigma x^2 . \Sigma y^2)}}$$

where $x =$ the deviations of X-scores from their mean,
$y =$ the deviations of Y-scores from their mean.

Just as there are different methods of calculating standard deviation, so there are different methods of calculating the correlation coefficient. Devices such as changing the origin of measurement and changing the size of the unit can ease the burden of calculation.

Correlation Coefficient for List of Marks

Method I.   Where $r = \dfrac{\Sigma xy}{\sqrt{(\Sigma x^2 . \Sigma y^2)}}$

The calculation of the correlation coefficient by this formula is illustrated from the following example in which the marks of twelve pupils in test X and test Y are to be compared.

Pupil	Test X	Test Y	x	y	xy	x^2	y^2
A	73	40	11	10	110	121	100
B	71	35	9	5	45	81	25
C	70	33	8	3	24	64	9
D	67	27	5	−3	−15	25	9
E	64	29	2	−1	−2	4	1
F	61	31	−1	1	−1	1	1
G	61	30	−1	0	0	1	0
H	60	26	−2	−4	8	4	16
I	58	28	−4	−2	8	16	4
J	56	34	−6	4	−24	36	16
K	53	25	−9	−5	45	81	25
L	50	22	−12	−8	96	144	64
					336		
					−42		
TOTALS	744	360			294	578	270

$M_x = 62$; $M_y = 30$; $\Sigma xy = 294$; $\Sigma x^2 = 578$; $\Sigma y^2 = 270$

Steps in Calculation

Step 1. Calculate the average mark in each set of marks:
$$M_x = 62 \qquad M_y = 30$$

Step 2. Find the deviation of each mark from its mean. These
are shown in columns headed x and y:
$$x = X - M_x \qquad y = Y - M_y$$

Step 3. Multiply the respective deviations x and y to give xy, and
find Σxy, having regard to signs:
$$\Sigma xy = 336 - 42$$
$$= 294$$

Step 4. Square each of the deviations and find their totals:
$$\Sigma x^2 = 578 \qquad \Sigma y^2 = 270$$

Step 5. The formula $r = \dfrac{\Sigma xy}{\sqrt{\Sigma x^2}\sqrt{\Sigma y^2}}$ gives:

$$r = \frac{294}{\sqrt{578}\sqrt{270}}$$
$$= \frac{294}{\sqrt{156060}}$$
$$= \frac{294}{395}$$
$$= 0.74$$

It may be concluded that the relationship between test X and
test Y is high.

Method II

The previous example gave the average of each set of marks
as a whole number. If the average had been a mixed number,
e.g. 62·35, the calculation would have been more laborious. It is
possible, however, to avoid this by choosing an assumed mean and
making the necessary corrections.

Suppose in the previous example the assumed means had been
taken as 61 and 31. The calculation would then be as follows:

Pupil	Test X	Test Y	d_x	d_y	d_xd_y	d_x^2	d_y^2
A	73	40	+12	+9	108	144	81
B	71	35	+10	+4	40	100	16
C	70	33	+9	+2	18	81	4
D	67	27	+6	−4	−24	36	16
E	64	29	+3	−2	−6	9	4
F	61	31	0	0	0	0	0
G	61	30	0	−1	0	0	1
H	60	26	−1	−5	5	1	25
I	58	28	−3	−3	9	9	9
J	56	34	−5	+3	−15	25	9
K	53	25	−8	−6	48	64	36
L	50	22	−11	−9	99	121	81
			40	18	327		
			−28	−30	−45		
TOTALS			12	−12	282	590	282

$N = 12$

$\Sigma d_x = 12 \quad \Sigma d_y = -12 \quad \Sigma d_xd_y = 282$

$\Sigma d_x^2 = 590 \quad \Sigma d_y^2 = 282$

Steps in Calculation

Step 1. Choose an assumed mean for each set of marks:

$$A_x = 61 \quad A_y = 31$$

Step 2. Find the deviation of each mark from its assumed mean, i.e. $d_x = X - A_x$, $d_y = Y - A_y$

Step 3. Find the sums of the deviations paying attention to signs:

$$\Sigma d_x = 12 \text{ and } \Sigma d_y = -12$$

Step 4. Multiply the respective deviations, having regard to signs to give Σd_xd_y.

Step 5. Find $\Sigma d_xd_y = 282$

Step 6. Square each of the deviations d_x^2 and d_y^2 and find the respective totals Σd_x^2 and Σd_y^2

$$\Sigma d_x^2 = 590 \text{ and } \Sigma d_y^2 = 282$$

Step 7. Calculate r from the formula

$$r = \frac{\Sigma d_x d_y - N a_x a_y}{\sqrt{(\Sigma d_x^2 - N a_x^2)} \sqrt{(\Sigma d_y^2 - N a_y^2)}}$$

$$\text{Where } a_x = \frac{\Sigma d_x}{N} \quad \text{and} \quad a_y = \frac{\Sigma d_y}{N}$$

$$= \frac{12}{12} \qquad\qquad = \frac{-12}{12}$$

$$= 1 \qquad\qquad = -1$$

$$\therefore \ a_x^2 = 1 \qquad a_y^2 = 1$$

$$r = \frac{282 - 12 \times 1 \times (-1)}{\sqrt{(590 - 12 \times 1)} \sqrt{(282 - 12 \times 1)}}$$

$$= \frac{282 + 12}{\sqrt{(590 - 12)} \sqrt{(282 - 12)}}$$

$$= \frac{294}{\sqrt{578} \sqrt{270}}$$

$$= \frac{294}{\sqrt{156060}}$$

$$= \frac{294}{395}$$

$$= 0 \cdot 74$$

Method III

Where a calculating machine or a book of tables is available there is another method of calculation with the product-moment formula.

$$r = \frac{N \Sigma X Y - \Sigma X \Sigma Y}{\sqrt{[N \Sigma X^2 - (\Sigma X)^2]} \sqrt{[N \Sigma Y^2 - (\Sigma Y)^2]}}$$

where ΣX and ΣY are the sums of the scores, ΣX^2 and ΣY^2 are the sums of the squares of the scores and N is the number of cases.

The calculation is illustrated with the same example used in Methods I and II.

Pupil	Test X	Test Y	XY	X^2	Y^2
A	73	40	2920	5329	1600
B	71	35	2485	5041	1225
C	70	33	2310	4900	1089
D	67	27	1809	4489	729
E	64	29	1856	4096	841
F	61	31	1891	3721	961
G	61	30	1830	3721	900
H	60	26	1560	3600	676
I	58	28	1624	3364	784
J	56	34	1904	3136	1156
K	53	25	1325	2809	625
L	50	22	1100	2500	484
TOTALS	744	360	22614	46706	11070

Steps in Calculation

Step 1. Find the sums of the individual marks: i.e.
$$\Sigma X = 744 \text{ and } \Sigma Y = 360$$

Step 2. Multiply the mark of each pupil in Test X by the corresponding mark in Test Y to give XY.

Step 3. Find ΣXY:
$$\Sigma XY = 22,614.$$

Step 4. Square the mark of each pupil in Test X to give X^2 and find ΣX^2:
$$\Sigma X^2 = 46,706.$$

Step 5. Square the mark of each pupil in Test Y to give Y^2 and find ΣY^2:
$$\Sigma Y^2 = 11,070.$$

Step 6. Find the correlation coefficient from the formula:

$$r = \frac{n\Sigma XY - \Sigma X \Sigma Y}{\sqrt{[N\Sigma X^2 - (\Sigma X)^2]}\sqrt{[N\Sigma Y^2 - (\Sigma Y)^2]}}$$

$$= \frac{12 \times 22614 - 744 \times 360}{\sqrt{[12 \times 46706 - (744)^2]}\sqrt{[12 \times 11070 - (360)^2]}}$$

$$= \frac{271368 - 267840}{\sqrt{(560472 - 553536)}\sqrt{(132840 - 129600)}}$$

$$= \frac{271368 - 267840}{\sqrt{6936} \times \sqrt{3240}}$$

$$= \frac{3528}{83 \cdot 3 \times 56 \cdot 9}$$

$$= \frac{3528}{4731}$$

$$= 0 \cdot 74$$

The correlation coefficient by each method is the same, i.e. 0·74.

Exercises

1. Find the correlation coefficient between the test scores in the English test (X) and arithmetic test (Y) of twenty pupils.

Pupil	X	Y	Pupil	X	Y
A	89	70	K	94	85
B	96	87	L	82	69
C	92	87	M	74	79
D	83	77	N	55	54
E	84	80	O	71	73
F	82	84	P	56	56
G	84	71	Q	47	46
H	92	87	R	51	68
I	83	71	S	39	38
J	73	85	T	68	64

2. Find the correlation coefficient between the following scores:

Pupil	A	B	C	D	E	F	G	H	I	J	K	L
Test X	73	71	70	67	64	61	61	60	58	56	53	50
Test Y	40	35	33	27	29	31	30	26	28	34	25	22

Correlation Coefficient for Grouped Data

The Scatter Diagram or Correlation Grid

The making of a scatter diagram or correlation grid is illustrated from the following example:

Pupil	I.Q.	English mark	Pupil	I.Q.	English mark
A	112	73	U	106	58
B	88	55	V	98	69
C	115	78	W	109	79
D	131	88	X	94	58
E	105	68	Y	108	74
F	91	50	Z	89	62
G	85	44	AA	105	68
H	106	62	BB	118	81
I	83	55	CC	103	67
J	102	71	DD	89	53
K	101	77	EE	111	68
L	87	47	FF	83	47
M	98	55	GG	123	86
N	103	69	HH	108	82
O	90	50	II	92	56
P	115	81	JJ	134	84
Q	113	94	KK	90	51
R	93	53	LL	110	78
S	83	53	MM	100	55
T	103	76	NN	113	78

The scatter diagram is a "grid" with one side representing the distribution of I.Q.s and the other the distribution of English marks. If the vertical sides represent from bottom to top I.Q.s it will show the range from 80 to 134 divided into 11 class-intervals. The horizontal side from left to right will show English marks ranging from 40 to 94 divided into the same number of class-intervals starting with 40–44.

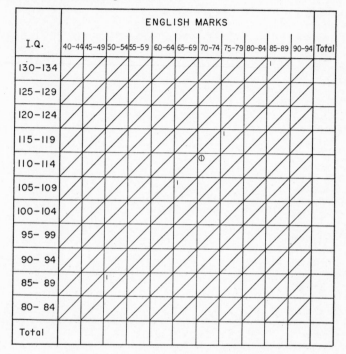

FIGURE 24.   Correlation grid for I.Q.s and English marks.

Pupil 1 has an I.Q. 112 and an English mark 73, hence his mark can be represented by a tally shown circled in the cell formed by the row 110–114 and the column 70–74. Similarly each pupil's I.Q. and English mark can be registered in the appropriate cell.

The registration of the first five pupils is shown in Figure 24. Once all the marks have been registered the tallies are added and the appropriate numbers recorded in each cell. The completed grid shown in Figure 25 is sometimes referred to as a *Scatter Diagram.*

The totals of the cell frequencies of the rows give the frequency distribution of the I.Q.s and the totals of all frequencies of

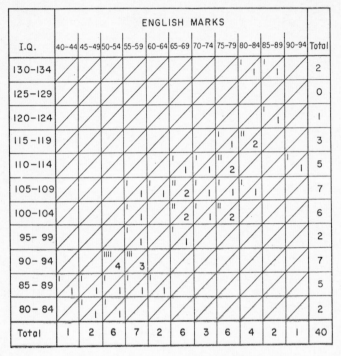

FIGURE 25. Scatter diagram for I.Q.s and English marks

the columns give the frequency distribution of the English marks.

The totals of the diagonal cell frequencies (from high-high to low-low) are also required as shown in Figure 26.

Method of Calculation

A data sheet or correlation chart is shown on page 102; the complete calculation can be made on such prepared sheets. From the calculation the means and standard deviations of I.Q.s

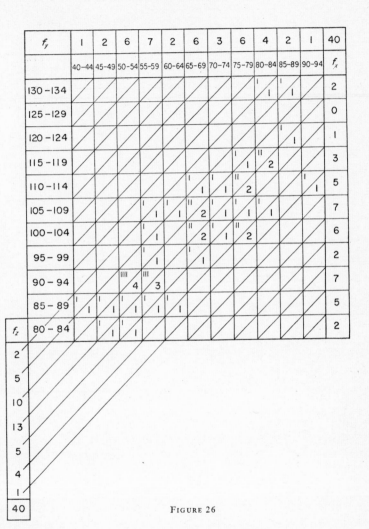

FIGURE 26

CORRELATION CHART

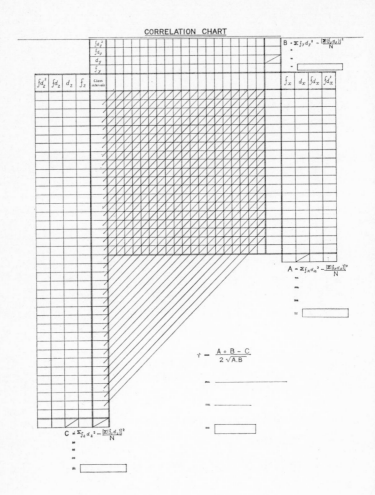

and English marks can readily be found. For example, the mean

I.Q. would be $107 + \left(\dfrac{-37}{40}\right) \times 5$

$$= 107 - 4 \cdot 63$$
$$= 102 \cdot 37$$

and the standard deviation

$$\sqrt{\left[\dfrac{283}{40} - \left(\dfrac{37}{40}\right)_2\right]} \times 5$$
$$= \sqrt{(7 \cdot 08 - 0 \cdot 86)} \times 5$$
$$= \sqrt{(6 \cdot 22)} \times 5$$
$$= 2 \cdot 49 \times 5$$
$$= 12 \cdot 45$$

In Figure 26, the frequencies of the rows, i.e. I.Q.s, are denoted by f_x, the frequencies of columns, i.e. English marks, are denoted by f_y, and the frequencies of the diagonals by f_z.

Calculate for each frequency, denoting I.Q.s by A, English marks by B, and diagonals by C. $\Sigma f d^2 - \dfrac{(\Sigma f d)^2}{N}$,

where $\Sigma f d^2$ is the sum of the squares of the deviations,

$\Sigma f d$ is the sum of the deviations,

N is the number of cases.

Then $A = \Sigma f_x d_x{}^2 - \dfrac{(\Sigma f_x d_x)^2}{N}$

$$B = \Sigma f_y d_y{}^2 - \dfrac{(\Sigma f_y d_y)^2}{N}$$

$$C = \Sigma f_z d_z{}^2 - \dfrac{(\Sigma f_z d_z)^2}{N}$$

The formula for r is then

$$r = \dfrac{A + B - C}{2\sqrt{(AB)}}.$$

	A				B				C		
f_x	d_x	$f_x d_x$	$f_x(d_x)^2$	f_y	d_y	$f_y d_y$	$f_y d_y^2$	f_z	d_z	$f_z d_z$	$f_z d_z^2$
2	5	10	50	1	5	5	25	2	3	6	18
0	4	0	0	2	4	8	32	5	2	10	20
1	3	3	9	4	3	12	36	10	1	10	10
3	2	6	12	6	2	12	24	13	0		0
5	1	5	5	3	1	3	3	5	−1	−5	5
7	0		0	6	0		0	4	−2	−8	16
6	−1	−6	6	2	−1	−2	2	1	−3	−3	9
2	−2	−4	8	7	−2	−14	28				
7	−3	−21	63	6	−3	−18	54				
5	−4	−20	80	2	−4	−8	32				
2	−5	−10	50	1	−5	−5	25				
		−61				−47				−16	
		24				40				+26	
40		−37	283	40		−7	261	40		+10	78

$$\Sigma f_x d_x = -37 \qquad \Sigma f_y d_y = -7 \qquad \Sigma f_z d_z = 10$$

$$\Sigma f_x d_x^2 = 283 \qquad \Sigma f_y d_y^2 = 261 \qquad \Sigma f_z d_z^2 = 78$$

$$A = \Sigma f_x d_x^2 - \frac{(\Sigma f_x d_x)^2}{N} \quad B = \frac{\Sigma f_y d_y - (\Sigma f_y d_y)^2}{N} \quad C = \Sigma f_z d_z^2 - \frac{(\Sigma f_z d_z)^2}{N}$$

$$= 283 - \frac{37^2}{40} \qquad\qquad = 261 - \frac{(-7)^2}{40} \qquad = 78 - \frac{(10)^2}{40}$$

$$= 283 - 34 \qquad\qquad\qquad = 261 - 1\cdot23 \qquad\quad = 78 - 2\cdot5$$

$$= 249 \qquad\qquad\qquad\quad \simeq 260 \qquad\qquad\quad = 75\cdot5$$

$$r = \frac{A + B - C}{2\sqrt{(AB)}} = \frac{249 + 260 - 75\cdot5}{2\sqrt{(249 \times 260)}}$$

$$= \frac{433\cdot5}{2\sqrt{64740}}$$

$$= \frac{433\cdot5}{2 \times 254\cdot5}$$

$$= \frac{433\cdot5}{509}$$

$$= 0\cdot85$$

Exercises

The following table gives the arithmetic marks as well as the I.Q.s and English marks of the 40 pupils listed on page 98. Calculate the correlation coefficient between I.Q. and arithmetic and between English and arithmetic.

Pupil	Mark	Pupil	Mark
A	77	U	70
B	44	V	80
C	73	W	62
D	68	X	64
E	59	Y	66
F	50	Z	36
G	55	AA	74
H	57	BB	79
I	50	CC	76
J	68	DD	55
K	65	EE	69
L	59	FF	42
M	64	GG	75
N	64	HH	91
O	50	II	50
P	79	JJ	97
Q	85	KK	61
R	50	LL	91
S	44	MM	69
T	68	NN	70

Application of the Correlation Coefficient

Reliability

The reliability of a test or examination is the consistency with which the test or examination yields its results. A reliable test gives marks which differ little from the marks of a retest or of an alternative form of test.

Three of the methods of determining the reliability of a test or examination are: (a) to give pupils a repetition of the same test at a later date, (b) to set an alternative test or examination of the same kind to the same pupils, and (c) to divide the test into two equal parts and compare the marks of each section.

(a) Test-retest

In the Scottish Mental Survey of 1931 when one school was tested twice by mistake, the correlation between the two sets of I.Q.s was 0·920, showing that the test had a high degree of reliability.

This method of assessing the reliability is open to the objection that pupils will react to the same test in different ways. Memory and practice effects will vary among the pupils and the transfer effects will not be constant. If the interval between test and retest is too long pupils will come to the second application of the test with different effects of maturation and teaching.

(b) Alternative of Parallel Forms of Tests

Provided that the parallel questions in each of the tests are of equal difficulty this method avoids the main anxieties of the test-retest method. There will be, however, a certain amount of memory and practice effect.

(c) Split-half

The test or examination is split into two equal parts and the correlation between the results of the two halves is calculated. This is generally regarded as the best method of computing the reliability of a test, although care has to be taken to ensure that the order of difficulty of the questions is accurately determined.

Unreliability is caused by several factors:

(a) There is the unreliability of the pupils. Changes occur in the feelings and the health of the children and they seldom approach two examinations or tests in the same frame of mind.

(b) The test itself may be unreliable. If the order of difficulty is not carefully arranged an early difficult question may upset some pupils more than others. Again, if the sample of the field of study is a bad one, pupils will not do themselves justice: this is particularly true of subjects where the curriculum is widespread as, for instance, in literature and history. Questions can be asked on a topic which the pupil has not studied, although a good examination should ensure that the questions are within every pupil's experience.

(c) There is unreliability of marking. Objective tests are constructed so that the examiners all give the same mark for each answer. The essay type of examination on the other hand is subject to wide variations in marking. Even the same examiner marking the same scripts at intervals can produce correlations as low as 0.3 between his sets of marks.

Validity

The validity of a test or examination is the fidelity with which it measures what it purports to measure. A clear distinction has to be made between reliability and validity. Scales which are "out" by a pound are reliable in so far as they consistently record weights as a pound more than they are, but these are not valid weights. An essay marked by deducting a mark for each spelling error will give reliable results no matter who marks the essay but this is not a valid method of assessing pupils' skill in writing English.

The validity of a test or examination is measured by finding the correlation between the marks scored by pupils in it and those attained by the same pupils on some other independent criterion of what the test or examination purports to measure.

Teachers should always establish the purpose of the examinations which they set. Examinations have in general three main objectives. They are: (a) a measure of attainment, (b) a means of diagnosis, and (c) a method of prediction.

(a) most examinations are measures of attainment. They attempt to find out how much a pupil knows about a particular subject.

(b) diagnostic tests are given to find out what a pupil does not know about a subject. A diagnostic test in addition in arithmetic, for example, finds out the addition factors in which a pupil is weak.

(c) many examination results are used as predictors of future performances in later stages in education. Tests in English and arithmetic in the primary school have been used for many years as predictors of success in secondary courses and leaving certificate examinations are used to give an estimate of a pupil's probable success at university. The correlations between examinations at the different stages in education are much lower than many teachers imagine.

Prediction

If the correlation between two sets of marks X and Y is r_{xy}, the relationship between them is expressed by the equation $Z_x = r_{xy}Z_y$. Where Z_x and Z_y are the standard scores of X and Y. Expanded into terms of raw scores the equation becomes

$$\frac{X-M_x}{\sigma_x} = r_{xy}\frac{(Y-M_y)}{\sigma_y}$$

hence $\quad X - M_x = r_{xy}\frac{\sigma_x}{\sigma_y}(Y-M_y)$

$\therefore \qquad\qquad X = M_x + r_{xy}\frac{\sigma_x}{\sigma_y}(Y-M_y)$

For example, if the correlation between I.Q.s and arithmetic marks is 0·80 and the mean I.Q. is 100 with σ,15, and the mean arithmetic mark is 65, with σ,10, what is the probable arithmetic mark of a pupil with I.Q. 105?

In the above equation

$$r_{xy} = 0\cdot80 \qquad M_y = 100 \qquad \sigma_y = 15$$
$$M_y = 65 \qquad \sigma_x = 10$$
$$X = 65 + 0\cdot8 \times \frac{10}{15}(105-100)$$
$$= 65 + 0\cdot8\,\frac{10}{15} \times 5$$
$$= 65 + 2\cdot7$$
$$= 67\cdot7$$

Exercises

1. The correlation coefficient between a group intelligence test (mean, 100; σ, 15) and an English test (mean, 50; σ, 10) is 0·85,

   (a) What English scores would you predict for pupils with I.Q. 85, 100 and 120?

   (b) What I.Q. would you predict for pupils scoring English marks of 45, 50 and 75?

2. Calculate the correlation coefficient ρ between the following marks. Calculate the correlation coefficient r by one of the product-moment formula.

Pupil	English	Arithmetic
A	88	72
B	95	85
C	97	82
D	82	77
E	93	81
F	86	81
G	87	77
H	94	83
I	83	78
J	81	84
K	92	80
L	84	70
M	77	74
N	54	53
O	75	74
P	60	57
Q	45	45
R	48	69
S	40	39
T	69	68

What is the degree of relationship between the marks?

3. What is the correlation coefficient between the two I.Q.s of the following 44 pupils?

Pupil	I.Q.1	I.Q.2	Pupil	I.Q.1	I.Q.2
A	114	118	W	92	100
B	124	126	X	95	103
C	118	116	Y	101	109
D	115	108	Z	91	94
E	125	119	AA	81	70
F	120	128	BB	95	92
G	129	120	CC	99	100
H	123	122	DD	101	93
I	117	112	EE	90	94
J	118	115	FF	86	92
K	122	121	GG	91	86
L	114	113	HH	101	101
M	105	107	II	99	97
N	81	91	JJ	79	73
O	98	98	KK	98	100
P	102	90	LL	93	88
Q	77	72	MM	95	93
R	101	93	NN	98	97
S	79	73	OO	112	110
T	103	105	PP	90	89
U	108	108	QQ	103	96
V	77	71	RR	77	71

4. What is the correlation coefficient between the scaled estimates in English and arithmetic of the 44 pupils?

   (a) What arithmetic estimate would you predict for pupils with English estimates 80, 70 and 50?

   (b) What English estimate would you predict for pupils with arithmetic estimates of 80, 70 and 50?

Pupil	English	Arith.	Pupil	English	Arith.
A	85	70	W	62	59
B	94	87	X	63	63
C	96	85	Y	71	71
D	82	76	Z	59	61
E	91	84	AA	34	37
F	84	84	BB	57	54
G	84	76	CC	61	57
H	93	86	DD	64	56
I	83	79	EE	58	59
J	82	86	FF	55	64
K	90	82	GG	55	60
L	83	69	HH	60	63
M	76	71	II	67	58
N	56	53	JJ	47	49
O	74	71	KK	69	82
P	60	58	LL	56	57
Q	48	45	MM	57	52
R	51	68	NN	62	66
S	42	38	OO	75	65
T	67	67	PP	62	59
U	73	79	QQ	68	62
V	39	42	RR	38	34

CHAPTER X

Difference Between Means

A TEACHER sets an examination to two classes, one of boys and one of girls. How can she tell whether the boys have done better than the girls? Suppose the means of the two classes are respectively 62 and 60, does the difference of the two marks mean that there is a real or significant difference between the class averages? The averages by themselves do not provide sufficient evidence on which to base a judgement: the scatter of the marks in each class must also be known.

The mean or average is determined by the sum of individual marks. Its stability or likelihood of variation will depend on the number of marks. For example, the smaller the number of marks the greater will be the effect if one or two pupils do worse or better than usual in the examination. The greater the number of pupils in the group the less the results will be affected by variations in individual pupils' performance.

A similar problem arises when a teacher sets her class two successive examinations and wishes to know whether the standard of attainment in each examination is the same. If the respective class averages are 60 and 64, does this indicate a real or significant difference in the standards of attainment? In this instance, because the same set of pupils are involved there is a relationship between the two sets of examination marks. Therefore it is necessary not only to have information about the scatter of marks and the size of the group but also to take account of the correlation between the two sets of marks.

Three factors have thus to be taken into account in investigating whether means are significantly different. These are

(a) the scatter of marks,

(b) the size of the group, and

(c) the relationship between the marks.

It is beyond the scope of this book to attempt an explanation of the theoretical basis of the calculations which are made to assess the significance of the difference between two means. Three types of calculation are illustrated:

(a) where the marks are unrelated and the groups are large (over 50);

(b) where the marks are unrelated and the groups are small (under 50);

(c) where the marks are related.

Method of Calculation

The calculation in each case follows a similar pattern.

(i) the difference between the means is found, say, $M_a - M_b$;

(ii) a quantity known as the *standard error*, denoted by SE, is calculated from a formula which is given in each case,

(iii) the ratio $\dfrac{M_a - M_b}{\text{SE}}$ is found and is denoted by t_c, the calculated value of t,

(iv) a theoretical value of t, denoted by t_t, is found from Table 11 (page 118),

(v) where $t_c \geqq t_t$ the difference between the means can be regarded as significant. Where $t_c < t_t$ the difference between the means can be regarded as not significant and therefore due to chance.

Significance of Difference between Two Means

(a) Large Groups (over 50) when Marks are Unrelated

Suppose group A, of N_a pupils, and group B of N_b pupils have respective means of M_a and M_b, standard deviations σ_a and σ_b. The difference between the means is $M_a - M_b$. The standard error of the difference is calculated from the formula.

$$SE = \sqrt{\left(\frac{\sigma_a^2}{N_a} + \frac{\sigma_b^2}{N_b}\right)}$$

$$\text{hence} \quad t_c = \frac{M_a - M_b}{\sqrt{\left(\frac{\sigma_a^2}{N_a} + \frac{\sigma_b^2}{N_b}\right)}}$$

Example: A group of 98 boys in School A has a mean I.Q. of 102 with standard deviation 14, and a group of 72 girls in school B a mean I.Q. of 100 with standard deviation 12. Is the mean I.Q. of the boys significantly different from that of the girls?

	Mean	σ	N
A	102	14	98
B	100	12	72

Difference of means $M_a - M_b = 102 - 100$
$$= 2$$

Standard error of difference

$$SE = \sqrt{\left(\frac{\sigma_a^2}{N_a} + \frac{\sigma_b^2}{N_b}\right)}$$
$$= \sqrt{\left(\frac{196}{98} + \frac{144}{72}\right)}$$
$$= \sqrt{(2+2)}$$
$$= \sqrt{4}$$
$$= 2$$
$$t_c = \frac{M_a - M_b}{SE}$$
$$= \frac{2}{2}$$
$$= 1$$

Where the groups are greater than 50, t_t can be taken as 2. In this example $t_c < 2$, therefore $t_c < t_t$ hence the difference between the means is not significant. The boys cannot therefore be described as more intelligent than the girls.

Exercise

1. In a school 90 boys and 80 girls were given an English test. The mean I.Q.s were 98 and 102 and the standard deviations 12 and 15, respectively. Are the means significantly different?
2. A teacher set an English examination to her classes each year. In one year 110 pupils had a mean score of 68 and a standard deviation of 11, whereas in the following year 100 pupils had a mean score of 65 with a standard deviation of 9. Is the difference in attainment between the two groups due to chance?

(b) Small Groups (under 50) when the Marks are Unrelated

A teacher has a class of 25 boys whose mean I.Q. is 110 and standard deviation is 15, and a class of 30 girls whose mean I.Q. is 115 and standard deviation 10. Are the girls more intelligent than the boys?

In this instance

$$\text{SE} = \sqrt{\left(\frac{(N_a \sigma_a{}^2 + N_b \sigma_b{}^2)\,(N_a + N_b)}{(N_a + N_b - 2)\,(N_a \times N_b)} \right)}$$

hence
$$t_c = \frac{M_a - M_b}{\sqrt{\left(\dfrac{(N_a \sigma_a{}^2 + N_b \sigma_b{}^2)\,(N_a + N_b)}{(N_a + N_b - 2)\,(N_a \times N_b)} \right)}}$$

$$= \frac{M_a - M_b}{\sqrt{(N_a \sigma_a{}^2 + N_b \sigma_b{}^2)}} \times \sqrt{\left(\frac{(N_a + N_b - 2) N_a N_b}{(N_a + N_b)} \right)}$$

and, if this value of t_c is greater than the value of t_t in Table 11 for the value of n given by $n = N_a + N_b - 2$, the difference between the means is significant, that is, the difference is not due to chance.

In the above example,

	Girls	Boys
Mean	115 (M_a)	110 (M_b)
σ	10 (σ_a)	15 (σ_b)
N	30 (N_a)	25 (N_b)

$$M_a - M_b = 115 - 110$$
$$= 5$$

$$\sqrt{(N_a\sigma_a{}^2 + N_b\sigma_b{}^2)} = \sqrt{(30 \times 100 \times 25 \times 225)}$$
$$= \sqrt{(3000 + 5626)}$$
$$= \sqrt{8625}$$
$$= 92 \cdot 87$$

$$\sqrt{\left(\frac{(N_a + N_b - 2)(N_a N_b)}{N_a + N_b}\right)} = \sqrt{\left(\frac{(30 + 25 - 2)(30 \times 25)}{30 + 25}\right)}$$
$$= \sqrt{\left(\frac{53 \times 30 \times 25}{55}\right)}$$
$$= \sqrt{\frac{39750}{55}}$$
$$= 26 \cdot 88$$

$$\text{therefore } t_c = \frac{5 \times 26 \cdot 88}{92 \cdot 87}$$
$$= \frac{134 \cdot 4}{92 \cdot 87}$$
$$= 1 \cdot 45$$

t_t is found from Table 11 by reading off the value of n corresponding to $n = N_a + N_b - 2$, $n = 30 + 25 - 2 = 53$. From Table 11 t_t for $n = 53$, lies between 2·01 and 2·00, hence the calculated t_c is smaller than this. The difference between the means is not significant and it cannot therefore be stated that the girls are more intelligent than the boys.

Exercises

1. In a term examination, 20 boys in a class have a mean score of 56 with standard deviation of 8, and 15 girls have a mean of 53 with standard deviation of 12. Are the means significantly different?

2. Which is the better achievement? 30 pupils with mean mark of 50 and standard deviation 10, or 20 pupils with mean mark 52 and standard deviation 12.

(c) Significance of Differences of Means between Related Groups

A teacher gives her class of 36 pupils a test in arithmetic and finds the mean mark is 50 and the standard deviation 12. A month later she sets a similar test and finds the mean mark is 60 and the standard deviation 8. The correlation coefficient between the two sets of marks is 0·60. Has there been a significant improvement in the arithmetic of her pupils?

In this instance

$$SE = \sqrt{\left(\frac{\sigma_a^2}{N_a} + \frac{\sigma_b^2}{N_b} - 2r_{ab} \frac{\sigma_a \sigma_b}{N_a N_b} \right)}$$

where r_{ab} is the correlation coefficient between the two sets of marks.

$$t_c = \frac{M_a - M_b}{\sqrt{\left(\frac{\sigma_a^2}{N_a} + \frac{\sigma_b^2}{N_b} - 2r_{ab} \frac{\sigma_a \sigma_b}{N_a N_b} \right)}}$$

and if this value of t_c is greater than the value of t_t in Table 11 for $n = N_a + N_b - 1$, the difference between the means is significant. In the above example

	First test	Second test
Mean	50 (M_b)	60 (M_a)
σ	12 (σ_b)	8 (σ_a)
N	36 (N_b)	36 (N_a)

$$M_b - M_a = 60 - 50$$
$$= 10$$

$$\frac{\sigma_a{}^2}{N_a} = \frac{64}{36} = 1{\cdot}78$$

$$\frac{\sigma_b{}^2}{N_b} = \frac{144}{36} = 4$$

$$2r_{ab}\frac{\sigma_a\sigma_b}{\sqrt{(N_aN_b)}} = 2 \times \frac{6}{10} \times \frac{8 \times 12}{\sqrt{(36 \times 36)}}$$

$$= \frac{2 \times 6 \times 8 \times 12}{10 \times 36}$$

$$= 3{\cdot}20$$

$$\sqrt{\left(\frac{\sigma_a{}^2}{N_a} + \frac{\sigma_b{}^2}{N_b} - 2r_{ab}\frac{\sigma_a\sigma_b}{N_aN_b}\right)} = \sqrt{(1{\cdot}78 + 4 - 3{\cdot}20)}$$

$$= \sqrt{2{\cdot}58}$$

$$= 1{\cdot}61$$

$$\therefore \quad t_c = \frac{10}{1{\cdot}61}$$

$$= 6{\cdot}21$$

From Table 11, t_t for $n = 36 + 36 - 1 = 71$, lies between 2 and 1·99, hence, as the calculated t_c is 7, the difference is significant. The pupils have made a real advance in their arithmetic scores.

TABLE 11

n	t_t	n	t_t	n	t_t	n	t_t
1	12·71	11	2·20	21	2·08	35	2.03
2	4·30	12	2·18	22	2·07	40	2·02
3	3·18	13	2·16	23	2·07	45	2·02
4	2·78	14	2·14	24	2·06	50	2·01
5	2·57	15	2·13	25	2·06	60	2·00
6	2·45	16	2·12	26	2·06	70	2·00
7	2·36	17	2·11	27	2·05	80	1·99
8	2·31	18	2·10	28	2·05	90	1·99
9	2·26	19	2·09	29	2·04		
10	2·23	20	2·09	30	2·04		

Exercises

1. A class of 35 pupils have an average mark of 68 with standard deviation 10 one term and next term an average mark of 72 with standard deviation 12. Is there a significant difference in their performance if the correlation coefficient between the term marks is 0·65.

2. In a spelling test of 20 questions 30 pupils make 250 errors. A similar test yields 300 errors. If the standard deviation of the two sets of scores is 2 and 3 respectively and the correlation coefficient between the results is 0·8, is the difference due to chance?

Appendices

Raw Score $= X$ Mean $= M$ Assumed Mean $= A$
Number of Scores $= N$
Deviation from Mean $= x = X - M$ (1)
Deviation from Assumed Mean $= d = X - A$ (2)
$X = d + A \ldots$ from (2)
Substitute for X in equation (1)

$\therefore \quad x = (d + A) - M$
$\therefore \quad x = d - (M - A)$
Let $M - A = a$ (3)
$\therefore \quad x = d - a$
$\therefore \quad x^2 = (d - a)^2$
$\therefore \quad x^2 = d^2 - 2ad + a^2$
$\therefore \quad \Sigma x^2 = \Sigma d^2 - 2a\Sigma d + Na^2$ (4)
$\quad\quad \Sigma d = \Sigma X - NA$ (from equation 2)

$\therefore \quad \Sigma d = \Sigma(M + x) - NA$ (since $X = M + x \ldots$ from
                                           equation 1)
$\therefore \quad \Sigma d = \Sigma M + \Sigma x - NA$
$\therefore \quad \Sigma d = NM + \Sigma x - NA$

But $\Sigma x = 0$ (as sum of positive deviations from mean is equal
            to sum of negative deviations from the mean)
$\therefore \quad \Sigma d = NM - NA$
$\therefore \quad \Sigma d = N(M - A)$
$\therefore \quad \Sigma d = Na$ (from equation 3)

$$\therefore \quad a = \frac{\Sigma d}{N}$$

Substitute for a in equation (4)

$$\therefore \quad \Sigma x^2 = \Sigma d^2 - 2\left(\frac{\Sigma d}{N}\right)\Sigma d + N\left(\frac{\Sigma d}{N}\right)^2$$

$$\therefore \quad \Sigma x^2 = \Sigma d^2 - 2\frac{(\Sigma d)^2}{N} + \frac{(\Sigma d)^2}{N}$$

$$\therefore \quad \Sigma x^2 = \Sigma d^2 - \frac{(\Sigma d)^2}{N}$$

$$\therefore \quad \frac{\Sigma x^2}{N} = \frac{\Sigma d^2}{N} - \frac{(\Sigma d)^2}{N^2}$$

$$\therefore \quad \sigma^2 = \frac{\Sigma d^2}{N} - \frac{(\Sigma d)^2}{N}$$

$$\therefore \quad \sigma = \sqrt{\left[\frac{\Sigma d^2}{N} - \left(\frac{\Sigma d}{N}\right)^2\right]}$$

APPENDIX II

Areas under the Normal Curve (expressed as proportions of the total area) between mean ordinate and ordinates at various sigma distances from the mean.

	·00	·01	·02	·03	·04	·05	·06	·07	·08	·09
0·0	·0000	·0040	·0080	·0120	·0160	·0199	·0239	·0279	·0319	·0359
0·1	·0398	·0438	·0478	·0517	·0557	·0596	·0636	·0675	·0714	·0753
0·2	·0793	·0832	·0871	·0910	·0948	·0987	·1026	·1064	·1103	·1141
0·3	·1179	·1217	·1255	·1293	·1331	·1368	·1406	·1443	·1480	·1517
0·4	·1554	·1591	·1628	·1664	·1700	·1736	·1772	·1808	·1844	·1879
0·5	·1915	·1950	·1985	·2019	·2054	·2088	·2123	·2157	·2190	·2224
0·6	·2257	·2291	·2324	·2357	·2389	·2422	·2454	·2486	·2517	·2549
0·7	·2580	·2611	·2642	·2673	·2704	·2734	·2764	·2794	·2823	·2852
0·8	·2881	·2910	·2939	·2967	·2995	·3023	·3051	·3078	·3106	·3133
0·9	·3159	·3185	·3212	·3238	·3264	·3290	·3315	·3340	·3365	·3389
1·0	·3413	·3438	·3461	·3485	·3508	·3531	·3554	·3577	·3599	·3621
1·1	·3643	·3665	·3686	·3708	·3729	·3749	·3770	·3790	·3810	·3830
1·2	·3849	·3869	·3888	·3907	·3925	·3944	·3962	·3980	·3997	·4015
1·3	·4032	·4049	·4066	·4082	·4099	·4115	·4131	·4147	·4162	·4177
1·4	·4192	·4207	·4222	·4236	·4251	·4265	·4279	·4292	·4306	·4319
1·5	·4332	·4345	·4357	·4370	·4383	·4394	·4406	·4418	·4429	·4441
1·6	·4452	·4463	·4474	·4484	·4495	·4505	·4515	·4525	·4535	·4545
1·7	·4554	·4564	·4573	·4582	·4591	·4599	·4608	·4616	·4625	·4633
1·8	·4641	·4649	·4656	·4664	·4671	·4678	·4686	·4693	·4699	·4706
1·9	·4713	·4719	·4726	·4732	·4738	·4744	·4750	·4756	·4761	·4767
2·0	·4772	·4778	·4783	·4788	·4793	·4798	·4803	·4808	·4812	·4817
2·1	·4821	·4826	·4830	·4834	·4838	·4842	·4846	·4850	·4854	·4857
2·2	·4861	·4864	·4868	·4871	·4875	·4878	·4881	·4884	·4887	·4890
2·3	·4893	·4896	·4898	·4901	·4904	·4906	·4909	·4911	·4913	·4916
2·4	·4918	·4920	·4922	·4925	·4927	·4929	·4931	·4932	·4934	·4936
2·5	·4938	·4940	·4941	·4943	·4945	·4946	·4948	·4949	·4951	·4952
2·6	·4953	·4955	·4956	·4957	·4959	·4961	·4961	·4962	·4963	·4964
2·7	·4965	·4966	·4967	·4968	·4969	·4970	·4971	·4972	·4973	·4974
2·8	·4974	·4975	·4976	·4977	·4977	·4978	·4979	·4979	·4980	·4981
2·9	·4981	·4982	·4982	·4983	·4984	·4984	·4985	·4985	·4986	·4986
3·0	·4987									
3·5	·4998									
4·0	·4999									

Ordinates under the Normal Curve (expressed as proportions of the mean ordinate) at various sigma distances from the mean.

	·00	·00	·02	·03	·04	·05	·06	·07	·08	·09
0·0	1·0000	1·0000	·9998	·9996	·9992	·9988	·9982	·9976	·9968	·9960
0·1	·9950	·9940	·9928	·9916	·9903	·9888	·9873	·9857	·9839	·9821
0·2	·9802	·9782	·9761	·9739	·9716	·9692	·9668	·9642	·9616	·9588
0·3	·9560	·9531	·9501	·9470	·9438	·9406	·9373	·9338	·9303	·9268
0·4	·9231	·9194	·9156	·9117	·9077	·9037	·8996	·8954	·8912	·8869
0·5	·8825	·8781	·8735	·8690	·8643	·8596	·8549	·8501	·8452	·8403
0·6	·8353	·8302	·8251	·8200	·8148	·8096	·8043	·7990	·7936	·7882
0·7	·7827	·7772	·7717	·7661	·7605	·7548	·7492	·7435	·7377	·7319
0·8	·7262	·7203	·7145	·7086	·7027	·6968	·6909	·6849	·6790	·6730
0·9	·6670	·6610	·6550	·6489	·6429	·6368	·6308	·6247	·6187	·6126
1·0	·6065	·6005	·5944	·5883	·5823	·5762	·5702	·5641	·5581	·5521
1·1	·5461	·5401	·5341	·5281	·5222	·5162	·5103	·5044	·4985	·4926
1·2	·4868	·4809	·4751	·4693	·4636	·4578	·4521	·4464	·4408	·4352
1·3	·4296	·4240	·4185	·4129	·4075	·4020	·3966	·3912	·3859	·3806
1·4	·3753	·3701	·3649	·3597	·3546	·3495	·3445	·3394	·3345	·3295
1·5	·3247	·3198	·3150	·3102	·3055	·3008	·2962	·2916	·2870	·2825
1·6	·2780	·2736	·2692	·2649	·2606	·2563	·2521	·2480	·2439	·2398
1·7	·2358	·2318	·2278	·2239	·2201	·2163	·2125	·2088	·2051	·2015
1·8	·1979	·1944	·1909	·1874	·1840	·1806	·1773	·1740	·1708	·1676
1·9	·1645	·1614	·1583	·1553	·1523	·1494	·1465	·1436	·1408	·1381
2·0	·1353	·1327	·1300	·1274	·1248	·1223	·1198	·1174	·1150	·1126
2·1	·1103	·1080	·1057	·1035	·1013	·0991	·0970	·0950	·0929	·0909
2·2	·0889	·0870	·0851	·0832	·0814	·0796	·0778	·0760	·0743	·0727
2·3	·0710	·0694	·0678	·0662	·0647	·0632	·0617	·0603	·0589	·0575
2·4	·0561	·0548	·0535	·0522	·0510	·0497	·0485	·0473	·0462	·0451
2·5	·0439	·0429	·0418	·0407	·0397	·0387	·0378	·0368	·0358	·0349
2·6	·0341	·0332	·0323	·0315	·0307	·0299	·0291	·0283	·0276	·0268
2·7	·0261	·0254	·0247	·0241	·0234	·0228	·0222	·0216	·0210	·0204
2·8	·0198	·0193	·0188	·0182	·0177	·0172	·0167	·0163	·0158	·0154
2·9	·0149	·0145	·0141	·0137	·0133	·0129	·0125	·0122	·0118	·0115
3·0	·0111									

APPENDIX IV

Table of squares and square roots of the numbers from 1 to 200.

Number	Square	Square Root	Number	Square	Square Root	Number	Square	Square Root
1	1	1·000	36	1296	6·000	71	5041	8·426
2	4	1·414	37	1369	6·083	72	5184	8·485
3	9	1·732	38	1444	6·164	73	5329	8·544
4	16	2·000	39	1521	6·245	74	5476	8·602
5	25	2·236	40	1600	6·325	75	5625	8·660
6	36	2·449	41	1681	6·403	76	5776	8·718
7	49	2·646	42	1764	6·418	77	5929	8·775
8	64	2·828	43	1849	6·557	78	6084	8·832
9	81	3·000	44	1936	6·633	79	6241	8·888
10	100	3·162	45	2025	6·708	80	6400	8·944
11	121	3·317	46	2116	6·782	81	6561	9·000
12	144	3·464	47	2209	6·856	82	6724	9·055
13	169	3·606	48	2304	6·928	83	6889	9·110
14	196	3·742	49	2401	7·000	84	7056	9·165
15	225	3·873	50	2500	7·071	85	7225	9·220
16	256	4·000	51	2601	7·141	86	7396	9·274
17	289	4·123	52	2704	7·211	87	7569	9·327
18	324	4·243	53	2809	7·280	88	7744	9·381
19	361	4·359	54	2916	7·348	89	7921	9·434
20	400	4·472	55	3025	7·416	90	8100	9·487
21	441	4·583	56	3136	7·483	91	8281	9·539
22	484	4·690	57	3249	7·550	92	8464	9·592
23	529	4·796	58	3364	7·616	93	8649	9·644
24	576	4·899	59	3481	7·681	94	8836	9·695
25	625	5·000	60	3600	7·746	95	9025	9·747
26	676	5·099	61	3721	7·810	96	9216	9·798
27	729	5·196	62	3844	7·874	97	9409	9·849
28	784	5·292	63	3969	7·937	98	9604	9·899
29	841	5·385	64	4096	8·000	99	9801	9·950
30	900	5·477	65	4225	8·062	100	10000	10·000
31	961	5·568	66	4356	8·124	101	10201	10·050
32	1024	5·657	67	4489	8·185	102	10404	10·100
33	1089	5·745	68	4624	8·246	103	10609	10·149
34	1156	5·813	69	4761	8·307	104	10816	10·198
35	1225	5·916	70	4900	8·367	105	11025	10·247

Number	Square	Square Root	Number	Square	Square Root	Number	Square	Square Root
106	11236	10·296	141	19881	11·874	176	30976	13·266
107	11449	10·344	142	20164	11·916	177	31329	13·304
108	11664	10·392	143	20449	11·958	178	31684	13·342
109	11881	10·440	144	20736	12·000	179	32041	13·379
110	12100	10·488	145	21025	12·042	180	32400	13·416
111	12321	10·536	146	21316	12·083	181	32761	13·454
112	12544	10·583	147	21609	12·124	182	33124	13·491
113	12769	10·630	148	21904	12·166	183	33489	13·528
114	12996	10·677	149	22201	12·207	184	33856	13·565
115	13225	10·724	150	22500	12·247	185	34225	13·601
116	13456	10·770	151	22801	12·288	186	34596	13·638
117	13689	10·817	152	23104	12·329	187	34969	13·675
118	13924	10·863	153	23409	12·369	188	35344	13·711
119	14161	10·909	154	23716	12·410	189	35721	13·748
120	14400	10·954	155	24025	12·450	190	36100	13·784
121	14641	11·000	156	24336	12·490	191	36481	13·820
122	14884	11·045	157	24649	12·530	192	36864	13·856
123	15129	11·091	158	24964	12·570	193	37249	13·892
124	15376	11·136	159	25281	12·610	194	37636	13·928
125	15625	11·180	160	25600	12·649	195	38025	13·964
126	15876	11·225	161	25921	12·689	196	38416	14·000
127	16129	11·269	162	26244	12·728	197	38809	14·036
128	16384	11·314	163	26569	12·767	198	39204	14·071
129	16641	11·358	164	26896	12·806	199	39601	14·107
130	16900	11·402	165	27225	12·845	200	40000	14·142
131	17161	11·446	166	27556	12·884			
132	17424	11·489	167	27889	12·923			
133	17689	11·533	168	28224	12·961			
134	17956	11·576	169	28561	13·000			
135	18225	11·619	170	28900	13·038			
136	18496	11·662	171	29241	13·077			
137	18769	11·705	172	29584	13·115			
138	19044	11·747	173	29929	13·153			
139	19321	11·790	174	30276	13·191			
140	19600	11·832	175	30625	13·229			

Answers

Chapter III

PAGES 10 and 11

No. 1				No. 2			
	12	//	2		65–69	///	3
	11	////// /	6		60–64	///	3
	10	/////	5		55–59	/////	5
	9	///	3		50–54	/////	5
	8	///	3		45–49	///// ////	9
	7	/////	5		40–44	///// /	6
	6	////	4		35–39	//	2
	5	//	2		30–34	/	1
	4	//	2		25–29	//	2
	3	//	2		20–24	/	1
	2		0		15–19	/	1
	1	/	1		10–14	/	1
	0		0		5–9	/	1
			35				40

PAGE 13

No. 1				No. 2		
95–99	//	2		98–104		0
90–94		0		91–97	//	2
85–89	//	2		84–90	//////	5
80–84	/	1		77–83	//////	5
75–79	////	4		70–76	////// ////	9
70–74		0		63–69	////// ////// /	11
65–69		0		56–62	//////	5
60–64	//	2		49–55	//	2
55–59	//	2		42–48	//	2
50–54	////// //	7		35–41	/	1
45–49	//////	5		28–34		0
40–44	///	3		21–27		0
35–39	/	1		14–20		0
30–34	//////	5		7–13		0
25–29		0		0–6		0
20–24	//////	5				―
15–19	/	1				42
10–14	/	1				―
5–9	/	1				
0–4		0				
		―				
		42				
		―				

PAGE 14

95–99	/	1
90–94	///	3
85–89	////	4
80–84	//	2
75–79	////// ///	8
70–74	////	4
65–69	////// //	7
60–64	//	2
55–59	////	4
50–54	///	3
45–49	/	1
40–44	//	2
35–39		0
30–34	/	1
25–29		0
		―
		42
		―

PAGE 20

1.
10	9	7	7	6	5	(a) 11
9	9	7	7	5	2	
9	8	7	6	5	0	(b) 7
9	8	7	6	5		
9	8	7	6	5		(c) 11

2.
10	/	1	
9		1	
8	ＭＨＴ ////	9	Mark 8
7	/	1	
6			
5	ＭＨＴ	5	
4	////	4	
3	//	2	
2	////	4	
1	/	1	
0			
		28	

3.
91–97	/	1	
84–90	////	4	
77–83	ＭＨＴ ///	8	
70–76	////	4	(a) 6
63–69	ＭＨＴ	5	
56–62	ＭＨＴ	5	(b) 8
49–55	ＭＨＴ ＭＨＴ	10	
42–48	///	3	
		40	

4.
90–98	///	3	
81–89	/	1	
72–80	ＭＨＴ ///	8	
63–71	ＭＨＴ ＭＨＴ //	12	12 pupils
54–62	ＭＨＴ //	7	
45–53	ＭＨＴ	5	
36–44	////	4	
		40	

Chapter IV

PAGE 22
1. $M = 7$ 2. $M = 29$ 3. $M = 54.8$

PAGE 23
1. $M = 6$
2. Mark

20	19	18	17	16	15	14	13	12	11	10	9	8	7	6	5
2	1	2	2	4	2	3	5	3	0	2	4	2	2	1	2

Frequency
$$M = 12.65$$

PAGE 30
English $M = 64.1$
Arithmetic $M = 66.4$

PAGE 35
1. 119.65
2. 84.3
3. English   57.05
   Arithmetic   38.88

Chapter V

PAGE 38
(a) 40   (b) 15.23

PAGE 39
$M = 69$ $\sigma = 9.695$

PAGE 43
2.38

PAGE 45
1. 9.0   2. 6.95

PAGES 47 and 48
1. $M = 67.45$ $\sigma = 15.2$
2. $M = 66.45$ $\sigma = 15.25$
3. $M = 99$ $\sigma = 14.665$
4. $M = 103.3$ $\sigma = 14.965$
5. $M = 57.05$ $\sigma = 26$
6. $M = 38.88$ $\sigma = 17.7$

Chapter VI

PAGE 50
1. 70 ($1\frac{1}{4}\sigma$)   67 ($1\frac{1}{3}\sigma$) $\therefore$ 67 is the better mark
2. 75 ($1\frac{1}{4}\sigma$)   70 ($1\frac{1}{2}\sigma$)   68 ($1\frac{1}{3}\sigma$), order 70, 68, 75

PAGE 51
(a) $1\frac{1}{3}\sigma$, 0, -2, $20 - \frac{1}{3}\sigma$.
(b) $-\frac{2}{3}\sigma$, -1σ, 0, 2σ.
(c) 130, 85, 80.5, 125.5.

PAGES 56 and 57

1. (a) Examination marks ($M40$, $\sigma20$), 76, 80, 84, 50, 38, 64
      Total estimated examination 158, 160, 162, 100, 78, 100
   (b) 119, 120, 121, 90, 79, 90

2. Order with raw marks D A C F H G E B
   Order with scaled marks A, D, C, F, H and G (equal), E, B

Chapter VII

PAGE 60
7, 10·5, 14·5, 17·5, 25, 28, 34, 54, 60, 85.

PAGE 63
2·5, 3·5, 5·17, 6·16, 6·83, 8·07.

PAGE 65

1. $P_{10} = 84·5$
   $P_{20} = 91·5$
   $P_{30} = 95·93$
   $P_{40} = 99·5$
   $P_{50} = 102$

   $P_{60} = 104·5$
   $P_{70} = 107·625$
   $P_{80} = 112$
   $P_{90} = 118·25$
   Interquartile range $= 15·19$

2. $P_{15} = 76·64$
   $P_{25} = 79·24$
   $P_{50} = 83·96$
   $P_{75} = 89·05$
   $P_{85} = 92·38$

PAGE 67

$P_{10} = 3·75$
$P_{20} = 5·5$
$P_{30} = 6·375$
$P_{40} = 7·1$
$P_{50} = 8·0$

$P_{60} = 9·17$
$P_{70} = 10·0$
$P_{80} = 10·67$
$P_{90} = 11·25$
$Q = 2·1825$

PAGE 71

1. 52, 58·25, 62·5, 66·5, 71·17, 76·17, 79·5, 82·3, 85·75.
2. 25·08, 40·98, 53·1.

Chapter VIII

1. 95·44
2. (a) 56·7%
   (b) 8·08%
   (c) 3·59%
3. (a) 75·05
   (b) 59·15–70·85
   (c) 52·4
4. (a) 25·14%
   (b) 92·2–107·8

1. (1) 0·4751
   (2) 0·8825
   (3) 0·0172
   (4) 0·4157
2. (1) 0·63
   (2) 0·92
   (3) 1·35
   (4) 1·795
   (5) 0·2583

Theoretical frequencies:

   0·633
   1·683
   3·518
   5·741
   7·461
   7·643
   6·176
   4·025
   1·994
   0·78
   0·245

Chapter IX

1. 0·97

2. 0·7617

1. 0·8053

2. 0·6975

1. 0·75, 2. 0·72

1. (a) 41·5, 50, 61·3
   (b) 93·625, 100, 131·875
2. 0·8274; 0·8993

3. 0·94
4. 0·91 (a) 75·32, 67·232, 51·04
       (b) 82·46, 72·229, 51·77
       (c) 58·54%

Chapter X

PAGE 115

1. $t_c = 1.904$ $t_t = 2$
   $\therefore t_c < t_t$
   Difference between means *not* significant.

2. $t_c = 2.170$ $t_t = 2$
   $\therefore t_c > t_t$
   Difference in attainment *not* due to chance.

PAGE 117

1. $t_c = 0.8602$ t_t lies between 2·04 and 2·03
   $\therefore t_c < t_t$
   Difference between means is *not* significant.

2. $t_c = 0.626$ t_t lies between 2·02 and 2·01
   $\therefore t_c < t_t$
   Neither achievement is better than the other.

PAGES 118 and 119

1. $t_c = 2.523$ $t_t = 2$
   $\therefore t_c > t_t$
   There is a significant difference.

2. $t_c = 4.967$ t_t lies between 2·01 and 2
   $\therefore t_c > t_t$
   Difference is not due to chance.

DATE DUE

r I